Biology

Prentice Hall

Teaching Resources
Unit 8

Copyright © by Pearson Education, Inc., publishing as Pearson Prentice Hall, Upper Saddle River, New Jersey. All rights reserved. Printed in the United States of America. This publication is protected by copyright, and permission should be obtained from the publisher prior to any prohibited reproduction, storage in a retrieval system, or transmission in any form or by any means, electronic, mechanical, photocopying, recording, or likewise. The publishers hereby grant permission to reproduce these pages, in part or in whole, for classroom use only, the number not to exceed the number of students in each class. Notice of copyright must appear on all copies. For information regarding permission(s), write to: Rights and Permissions Department.

Pearson Prentice Hall™ is a trademark of Pearson Education, Inc.
Pearson® is a registered trademark of Pearson plc.
Prentice Hall® is a registered trademark of Pearson Education, Inc.

PEARSON

Prentice
Hall

Upper Saddle River, New Jersey
Boston, Massachusetts

ISBN 0-13-203403-4

2 3 4 5 6 7 8 9 10   10 09 08 07

To the Teacher

The Teaching Resources unit booklets have been designed to help you teach *Prentice Hall Biology*. Each unit book consists of materials that have been designed to stimulate students' interest in biology, develop their critical thinking, and teach them basic science skills. The unit books will accommodate a wide range of student abilities and interests.

Each teaching resource unit book contains the following:

- Lesson Plans (for each section)
- Reading and Study Workbook A (includes section summaries, section worksheets, and a chapter vocabulary review written at grade level)
- Adapted Reading and Study Workbook B worksheets (Includes section summaries, key concept worksheets, and a chapter vocabulary review written at a sixth-grade level)
- Section Review Worksheets
- Enrichment Worksheets
- Graphic Organizers
- Chapter Tests (Includes two tests for each chapter—Test A for students performing on or above grade level; Test B for students performing on or below grade level)
- Unit Tests (two tests for each unit—Test A and Test B)
- Answer Key (for section review worksheets, enrichment worksheets, graphic organizers, and chapter tests.)
- Graphic Organizer Transparencies (generic reproducible masters)
- Transparency Planner (Full-color preview of all the transparencies that support the unit)

Unit 8 Invertebrates
Chapter 26 Sponges and Cnidarians

Lesson Plans
    Section 26-1 1
    Section 26-2 2
    Section 26-3 3
Adapted Reading and Study Workbook
    Section Summaries 4
    Early Animal Development 7
    Symmetry 8
    Sponges 9
    Sponge Life Cycle 10
    Cnidarian Body Forms 11
    Cnidocytes 12
    Cnidarian Life Cycle 13
    Vocabulary Review 14
Reading and Study Workbook
    Section Summaries 15
    Section 26–1 17
    Section 26–2 21
    Section 26–3 23
    Vocabulary Review 26
Review and Reinforce
    Section Review 26–1 27
    Section Review 26–2 28
    Section Review 26–3 29
    Chapter Vocabulary Review 30
Enrichment: The Portuguese Man-of-War 32
Graphic Organizer: Cycle Diagram 33
Chapter 26 Test A 34
Chapter 26 Test B 40

Chapter 27 Worms and Mollusks

Lesson Plans
    Section 27–1 44
    Section 27–2 45
    Section 27–3 46
    Section 27–4 47
Adapted Reading and Study Workbook
    Section Summaries 48
    Flatworm Development 51
    Flatworm Anatomy 52
    Annelid Anatomy 53
    Types of Worms 54
    Mollusk Body Plans 55
    Clam Anatomy 56
    Types of Mollusks 57
    Vocabulary Review 58

Reading and Study Workbook
    Section Summaries 59
    Section 27–1 61
    Section 27–2 64
    Section 27–3 66
    Section 27–4 69
    Vocabulary Review 72
Review and Reinforce
    Section Review 27–1 73
    Section Review 27–2 74
    Section Review 27–3 75
    Section Review 27–4 76
    Chapter Vocabulary Review 77
Enrichment: Leeches..79
Graphic Organizer: Concept Map 80
Chapter 27 Test A 81
Chapter 27 Test B 87

Chapter 28 Arthropods and Echinoderms

Lesson Plans
    Section 28–1 91
    Section 28–2 92
    Section 28–3 93
    Section 28–4 94
Adapted Reading and Study Workbook
    Section Summaries 95
    Arthropod Anatomy 98
    Crustacean Anatomy...99
    Spider Anatomy...100
    Most Animals are Insects..101
    Insects...102
    Complete and Incomplete Metamorphosis 103
    Types of Arthropods 104
    Echinoderm Anatomy...105
    Vocabulary Review 106
Reading and Study Workbook
    Section Summaries 107
    Section 28–1 109
    Section 28–2 112
    Section 28–3 115
    Section 28–4 118
    Vocabulary Review 120
Review and Reinforce
    Section Review 28–1 121
    Section Review 28–2 122
    Section Review 28–3 123
    Section Review 28–4 124
    Chapter Vocabulary Review 125
Enrichment: Life in Ant Colonies 127

Graphic Organizer: Compare/Contrast Table..128
Chapter 28 Test A..129
Chapter 28 Test B..135

Chapter 29 Comparing Invertebrates

Lesson Plans
    Section 29–1...139
    Section 29–2...140
Adapted Reading and Study Workbook
    Section Summaries..141
    Major Adaptations in Animal Evolution....................................144
    Comparing Invertebrates...145
    Coelom Evolution...146
    Invertebrate Digestive Systems...147
    Invertebrate Respiratory Systems..148
    Invertebrate Circulatory Systems...149
    Invertebrate Excretory Systems...150
    Invertebrate Nervous Systems...151
    Vocabulary Review..152
Reading and Study Workbook
    Section Summaries..153
    Section 29–1...155
    Section 29–2...159
    Vocabulary Review..162
Review and Reinforce
    Section Review 29–1..163
    Section Review 29–2..164
    Chapter Vocabulary Review...165
Enrichment: Animals of the Vendian Period..167
Graphic Organizer: Compare/Contrast Table..168
Chapter 29 Test A..169
Chapter 29 Test B..175

Unit 8 Test A...179
Unit 8 Test B...185
Answer Key...189
Graphic Organizer Transparencies
    Flowchart..197
    Modified Concept Map..198
    Cause/Effect..199
    Compare/Contrast..200
    Venn Diagram..201
    KWL Chart...202
Transparencies...203

LESSON PLAN 26–1 (pages 657–663)

Introduction to the Animal Kingdom

Section Objectives   **Local Standards**

- **26.1.1 List** the characteristics that all animals share.
- **26.1.2 Describe** the essential functions that animals carry out.
- **26.1.3 Identify** the important trends in animal evolution.

Vocabulary invertebrate • vertebrate • feedback inhibition • blastula • protostome • deuterostome • anus • endoderm • mesoderm • ectoderm • radial symmetry • bilateral symmetry • cephalization

1 FOCUS

Reading Strategy
Before reading, students brainstorm a list of every characteristic they know about animals.

Targeted Resources
❑ Transparencies: **396** Section 26–1 Interest Grabber
❑ Transparencies: **397** Section 26–1 Outline
❑ Transparencies: **398** Concept Map

2 INSTRUCT

Build Science Skills: Classifying
Students brainstorm a list of familiar animals and then classify each as a vertebrate or an invertebrate. **L1 L2**

Build Science Skills: Communicating Results
Students choose one of the essential functions and research how various animals carry out that function. **L2**

Use Visuals: Figure 26–3
Use Figure 26–3 to reinforce an understanding of animal evolution. **L1 L2**

Build Science Skills: Using Models
Students create models of early animal development, using modeling compound. **L2**

Quick Lab
With models, students relate bilateral symmetry with the ability to walk forward. **L2**

Targeted Resources
❑ Reading and Study Workbook: Section 26–1
❑ Adapted Reading and Study Workbook: Section 26–1
❑ Teaching Resources: Section Summaries 26–1, Worksheets 26–1
❑ Transparencies: **399** Figure 26–5 Body Symmetry
❑ **NSTA** *sci*LINKS Classifying animals

3 ASSESS

Evaluate Understanding
List the essential functions on the board, and then call on students to explain what each entails.

Reteach
Students create two flowcharts that explain early development, as in Figure 26–4.

Targeted Resources
❑ Teaching Resources: Section Review 26–1
❑ **iText** Section 26–1

LESSON PLAN 26–2 (pages 664–667)

Sponges

Time
1 period
1/2 block

Section Objectives

- **26.2.1 Explain** what a sponge is.
- **26.2.2 Describe** how sponges carry out essential functions.
- **26.2.3 Describe** the ecology of sponges.

Vocabulary choanocyte • osculum • spicule • archaeocyte • internal fertilization • larva • gemmule

Local Standards

---

1 FOCUS

Vocabulary Preview
Have students divide each Vocabulary word into its syllables.

Targeted Resources
- ❏ Transparencies: **400** Section 26–2 Interest Grabber
- ❏ Transparencies: **401** Section 26–2 Outline

---

2 INSTRUCT

Build Science Skills: Observing
Students observe with a hand lens a natural sponge and make drawings of what they see. **L2**

Use Visuals: Figure 26–8
Use Figure 26–8 to reinforce understanding of structure and function in sponges. **L2 L2**

Build Science Skills: Applying Concepts
Help students understand respiration and excretion in sponges. **L2**

Demonstration
Demonstrate how much water a natural sponge can hold by comparing the mass of water in a soaked natural sponge with a soaked synthetic sponge. **L2**

Use Visuals: Figure 26–10
Use Figure 26–10 to reinforce understanding of the ecology of sponges. **L2**

Targeted Resources
- ❏ Reading and Study Workbook: Section 26–2
- ❏ Adapted Reading and Study Workbook: Section 26–2
- ❏ Teaching Resources: Section Summaries 26–2, Worksheets 26–2
- ❏ Transparencies: **402** Sponge Life Cycle, **403** Figure 26–8 The Anatomy of a Sponge

---

3 ASSESS

Evaluate Understanding
Have students explain why sponges are animals and how sponges carry out each of the essential functions.

Reteach
Ask students to make their own drawings of Figure 26–8.

Targeted Resources
- ❏ Teaching Resources: Section Review 26–2
- ❏ *i* Text > Section 26–2

LESSON PLAN 26–3 (pages 669–675)

Cnidarians

Time
1 period
1/2 block

Section Objectives

Local Standards

- **26.3.1 Explain** what a cnidarian is.
- **26.3.2 Describe** the two body plans that exist in the cnidarian life cycle.
- **26.3.3 Describe** how cnidarians carry out essential functions.
- **26.3.4 Identify** the three groups of cnidarians.
- **26.3.5 Describe** the ecology of cnidarians.

Vocabulary cnidocyte • nematocyst • polyp • medusa • gastrovascular cavity • nerve net • hydrostatic skeleton • external fertilization

1 FOCUS

Reading Strategy
Have students write the section's boldface sentences in their notebooks and find information that supports each.

Targeted Resources
❑ Transparencies: **404** Section 26–3 Interest Grabber
❑ Transparencies: **405** Section 26–3 Outline

2 INSTRUCT

Use Visuals: 26–12
Use Figure 26–12 to reinforce an understanding of cnidarian anatomy. **L1 L2**

Demonstration
Use two plastic cups to demonstrate the differences in structure between a polyp and a medusa. **L1 L2**

Use Visuals: Figure 26–15
Use Figure 26–15 to review the life cycle of a jellyfish. **L2**

Build Science Skills: Comparing and Contrasting
Students organize information in a table about the three classes of cnidarians. **L2 L3**

Analyzing Data
Students analyze data in a table about the source of threats to coral reefs. **L2 L3**

Targeted Resources
❑ Reading and Study Workbook: Section 26–3
❑ Adapted Reading and Study Workbook: Section 26–3
❑ Transparencies: **406** Jellyfish Life Cycle, **407** Figure 26–12 The Polyp and Medusa Stages
❑ Teaching Resources: Section Summaries 26–3, Worksheets 26–3, Enrichment
❑ Lab Worksheets: Chapter 26 Exploration
❑ Lab Manual A: Chapter 26 Lab
❑ Lab Manual B: Chapter 26 Lab

3 ASSESS

Evaluate Understanding
Students classify specific cnidarians as members of one of the three classes.

Reteach
Students write a story of a year in the life of a jellyfish, using terms from the section.

Targeted Resources
❑ Teaching Resources: Section Review 26–3, Chapter Vocabulary Review, Graphic Organizer, Chapter 26 Tests: Levels A and B
❑ **iText** Section 26–3, Chapter 26 Assessment
❑ **PHSchool.com** Online Chapter 26 Test

Chapter 26   Sponges and Cnidarians

Summary

26–1 Introduction to the Animal Kingdom

All members of the animal kingdom share certain characteristics. **All animals are multicellular, eukaryotic heterotrophs whose cells lack walls.**

More than 95 percent of all animal species are grouped in one informal category: invertebrates. **Invertebrates** are animals that have no backbone, or vertebral column. The other 5 percent of animals are vertebrates. **Vertebrates** are animals with a backbone.

An animal's structure, or anatomy, allows it to carry out body functions. Many body functions help animals maintain homeostasis. Homeostasis is the process by which organisms keep internal conditions stable. Often this involves use of internal feedback mechanisms. For example, **feedback inhibition** occurs when the product of a process stops or limits the process itself.

Animals carry out the following essential functions:
- **Feeding** Animals must feed, or eat food. Herbivores eat plants, carnivores eat animals, and parasites live and feed on other organisms.
- **Respiration** All animals respire, or take in oxygen and give off carbon dioxide.
- **Circulation** Most animals have a system that circulates materials within their bodies.
- **Excretion** Most animals have an excretory system that helps eliminate wastes from the body.
- **Response** Animals respond to their environment using nerve cells.
- **Movement** Most animals move from place to place using muscles and some type of skeletal system.
- **Reproduction** Most animals reproduce sexually by producing haploid gametes. Sexual reproduction helps create and maintain genetic diversity in populations. Many invertebrates can reproduce asexually as well. Asexual reproduction produces offspring that are genetically identical to the parent.

Complex animals tend to have high levels of cell specialization and internal body organization. They also tend to have bilateral body symmetry, a front end or head with sense organs, and a body cavity.

- **Early Development** Animals that reproduce sexually start life as a fertilized egg, or zygote. The zygote divides several times to form a **blastula,** a hollow ball of cells. The blastula then folds in on itself to form a single opening called a blasto-pore. The blastopore leads to a central tube that becomes the digestive tract. In time, the blastopore forms either a mouth or an anus. The anus is the opening through which wastes leave the digestive tract. If the blastopore forms a mouth, the animal is a **protostome.** If the blastopore forms an anus, the animal is a **deuterstome.**

The cells of most animal embryos differentiate into three germ layers. The **endoderm** is the innermost germ layer. The middle layer is the **mesoderm.** The **ectoderm** is the outermost germ layer.

- **Body cavity formation** Most animals have a body cavity. A *body cavity* is a fluid-filled space that lies between the digestive tract and the body wall.
- **Body symmetry and cephalization** All animals, except sponges, show some type of body symmetry. In **radial symmetry,** any number of imaginary planes can be drawn through the center of the animal to divide it into equal halves. In **bilateral symmetry,** only one imaginary plane can divide the body into two equal halves. Animals with bilateral symmetry typically have cephalization. **Cephalization** is a concentration of sense organs and nerve cells at the front of the body. More complex animals have bilateral symmetry.

26–2 Sponges

Sponges make up the phylum Porifera. **Like all animals, sponges are multicellular and heterotrophic. They have no cell walls and have only a few specialized cells.** Sponges live their entire adult lives attached to a surface.

Sponges sift microscopic food particles from water moving through them. Specialized cells called **choanocytes** move a current of water through the sponge body. This water enters through pores in the body wall. It leaves through the **osculum,** a large hole at the top of the central cavity. Digestion is intracellular; it takes place inside cells. **The movement of water through a sponge also supplies a sponge with everything it needs for respiration, circulation, and excretion.**

Sponges reproduce both sexually and asexually. In sexual reproduction, eggs are fertilized internally. The zygote then develops into a larva. A **larva** is an immature stage of an organism that looks different from the adult form. The larva are motile. They are carried by ocean currents until they settle to the sea floor and grow into a mature sponge. Sponges reproduce asexually by budding.

26–3 Cnidarians

The phylum Cnidaria includes hydras, jellyfishes, sea anemones, and corals. **Cnidarians are soft-bodied carnivores that have stinging tentacles arranged in circles around their mouths. They are the simplest animals having body symmetry and specialized tissues.** Cnidarians exhibit radial symmetry. They have a central mouth surrounded by numerous tentacles. Cnidarians get their name from the cnidocytes, or stinging cells, on their tentacles.

Most cnidarians have a life cycle with two very different stages: a polyp and a medusa.
- A **polyp** has a cylindrical body with armlike tentacles and usually does not move. A polyp lives attached to a surface with its mouth pointing upward.
- A **medusa** has a bell-shaped body with a mouth at the bottom. Medusas are free-swimming.

A cnidarian has a **gastrovascular cavity**—a digestive chamber with one opening. Food and wastes enter and leave through this opening. Digestion is extracellular, meaning it takes place outside cells.

After digestion, nutrients are transported throughout the body by diffusion. Cnidarians take in oxygen and release wastes by diffusion through their body walls.

Cnidarians gather information from their environment using specialized sensory cells. Both polyps and medusas have a nerve net. A **nerve net** is a network of nerve cells that together let cnidarians detect stimuli.

Some cnidarians have a **hydrostatic skeleton.** This skeleton consists of a layer of circular muscles and a layer of longitudinal muscles that, together with the water in the gastrovascular cavity, enable the cnidarian to move.

Cnidarians reproduce both sexually and asexually. Polyps reproduce asexually by budding. Sexual reproduction takes place with external fertilization in water.

There are three classes of cnidarians. They include jellyfishes, hydras and their relatives, and sea anemones and corals.
- Jellyfishes live mostly as medusas.
- Hydras and related animals grow in branching colonies. The Portuguese man-of-war is a colonial hydrozoan composed of many specialized polyps.
- Sea anemones and corals have only the polyp stage in their life cycles. Most corals are colonial. Their polyps grow together in large numbers. As the colonies grow, they secrete an underlying skeleton of calcium carbonate (limestone). Coral colonies form structures called coral reefs.

Early Animal Development

During the early development of most animals, cells divide to form a hollow ball called a blastula. An opening, called a blastopore, forms. The blastopore of a protostome develops into a mouth. The blastopore of a deuterostome develops into an anus. Most early animal embryos differentiate into three layers of cells called germ layers. These three layers, from innermost to outer-most, are the *endoderm*, *mesoderm*, and *ectoderm*.

Color the endoderm *yellow and* ectoderm *blue. The mesoderm has already been shaded for you.*

Protostome

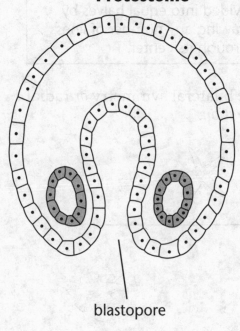

blastopore

Deuterostome

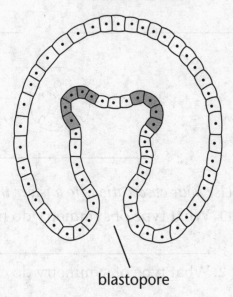

blastopore

Use the diagram to answer the questions.

1. Which germ layer develops into the lining of the digestive tract and the respiratory system?

_____

2. Which germ layer develops into the outer layer of skin?

_____

Symmetry

Study the information in the table.

Bilateral Symmetry	Radial Symmetry

An object or organism with bilateral symmetry can be divided into two matching halves at only one point.	An object or organism with radial symmetry can be divided into equal halves by drawing any number of lines through its center.

Look carefully at each animal below. Write bilateral symmetry *or* radial symmetry *on the line beneath each illustration.*

_____   _____

_____   _____

Use your observations to answer the question.

1. What type of symmetry do humans have?

_____

2. What type of symmetry do cats have?

_____

Sponges

A sponge moves water through its body in order to carry out basic life functions. It takes in water through its pores. Water leaves a sponge through a hole at its top called the osculum.

Look at the water flow arrow in the diagram on the right. Draw arrows to show the water flow into and out of the sponge in the left part of the illustration.

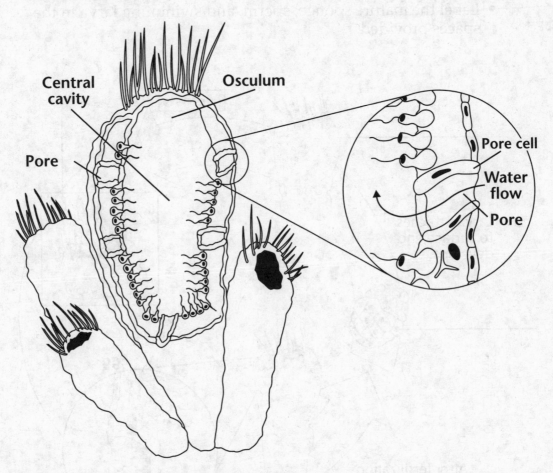

Name two basic life functions that sponges carry out by moving water through their bodies. One function has been identified for you.

1. circulation _____

2. _____

3. _____

Answer the question. Circle the correct answer.

1. What type of symmetry do sponges have?

   bilateral   radial   no symmetry

Sponge Life Cycle

Sponges can reproduce both sexually and asexually. For sexual reproduction, most sponges produce both sperm and eggs, but at different times. The steps involved in the sexual reproduction of sponges are diagrammed below.

Mark the life cycle of a sponge according to the statements below.

- Circle the part of the life cycle that shows internal fertilization.
- Label the mature sponge, sperm, and swimming larva in the spaces provided.

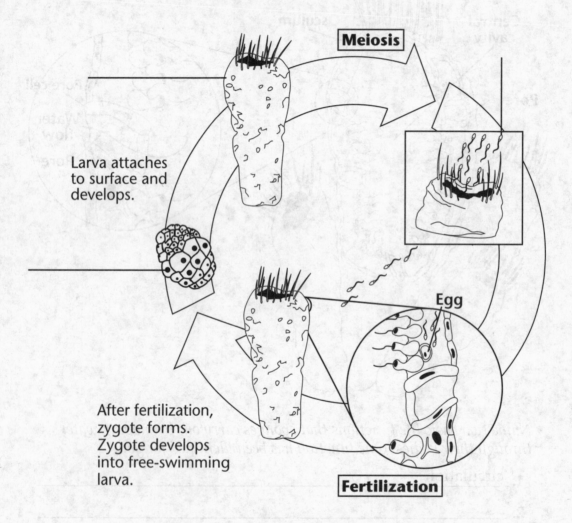

Answer the question.

1. What is a larva?

_____

_____

Cnidarian Body Forms

Most cnidarians have both a polyp and a medusa form during their life cycles.

Label the polyp *and* medusa *forms of the cnidarian pictured below. Then, circle the tentacles on each diagram.*

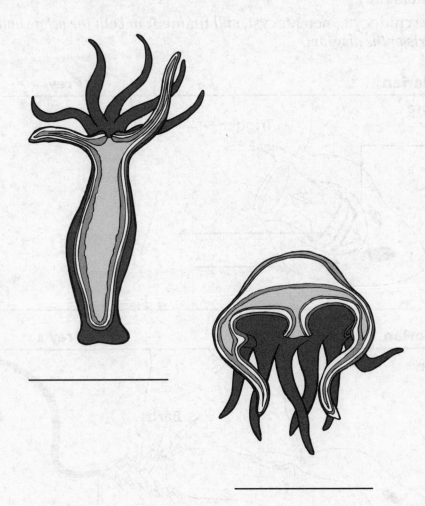

_____

_____

Use the illustrations to answer the questions.

1. What is the function of a cnidarian's tentacles?

_____

_____

2. Which body form shown above is motile?

_____

3. Which body form shown above is sessile?

_____

Cnidocytes

Along their tentacles, cnidarians have stinging cells called cnidocytes. They use these cells for defense and to capture prey. Cnidocytes contain poison-filled stinging structures called nematocysts. The drawing below shows a cnidocyte before and after it encounters prey.

Label the cnidocyte, nematocyst, *and* filament *in both the before and after parts of the diagram.*

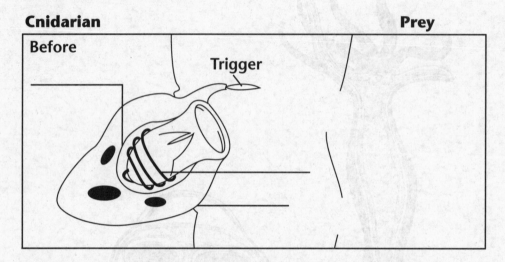

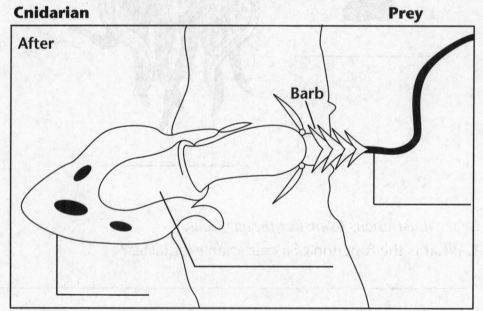

Use the drawing to answer the question.

1. What happens when prey comes in contact with the trigger?

_____

_____

Cnidarian Life Cycle

Most cnidarians can reproduce both asexually and sexually. The life cycle of a jellyfish is diagramed below. It involves both haploid and diploid stages.

Color the arrows showing haploid stages of the life cycle orange. Color the arrows showing diploid stages purple.

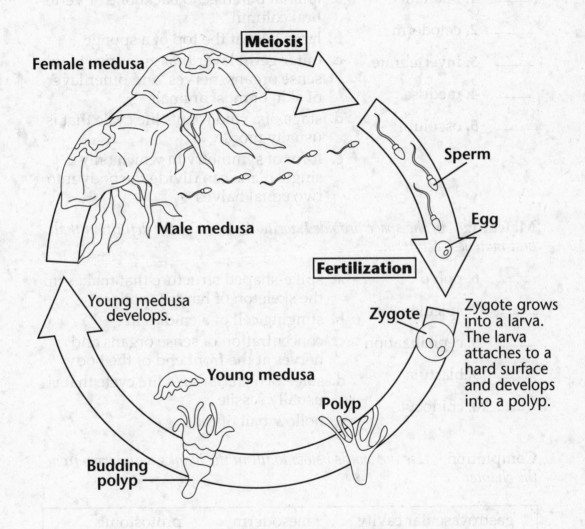

Use the drawing to answer the question. Circle the correct answer.

1. What forms as a result of meiosis?

    egg   polyp

Chapter 26   Sponges and Cnidarians

Vocabulary Review

Matching   *In the space provided, write the letter of the definition that best matches each term.*

_____ **1.** bilateral

_____ **2.** ectoderm

_____ **3.** invertebrate

_____ **4.** medusa

_____ **5.** osculum

a. animal that has no backbone or vertebral column

b. large hole at the top of a sponge

c. outer germ layer that gives rise to the sense organs, nerves, and outer layer of skin of most animals

d. stage of a cnidarian's life cycle that is usually motile

e. form of symmetry in which only a single plane can divide the body into two equal halves

Matching   *In the space provided, write the letter of the definition that best matches each term.*

_____ **6.** polyp

_____ **7.** spicule

_____ **8.** cephalization

_____ **9.** blastula

_____ **10.** cnidocyte

a. spike-shaped structure that makes up the skeleton of harder sponges

b. stinging cell of a cnidarian

c. concentration of sense organs and nerves at the front end of the body

d. stage of a cnidarian's life cycle that is usually sessile

e. hollow ball of cells

Completion   *Use the words below to fill in the blanks with terms from the chapter.*

gastrovascular cavity	mesoderm	protostome

11. An animal whose mouth is formed from the blastopore is a

_____.

12. The middle germ layer, or _____, gives rise to muscles and many organ systems.

13. The digestive chamber found in cnidarians is the

_____.

Chapter 26 Sponges and Cnidarians

Summary

26–1 Introduction to the Animal Kingdom

All members of the kingdom Animalia share certain characteristics. Animals are multicellular, eukaryotic heterotrophs whose cells lack cell walls. The bodies of most animals contain tissues. Over 95 percent of all animal species are often grouped in a single, informal category: invertebrates. Invertebrates are animals that do not have a backbone, or vertebral column. The other 5 percent of animals are called vertebrates, because they have a backbone.

Animals carry out the following essential functions: feeding, respiration, circulation, excretion, response, movement, and reproduction. The study of the functions of organisms is called physiology. The structure, or anatomy, of an animal's body enables it to carry out physiological functions.

Many body functions help animals maintain homeostasis. Homeostasis is often maintained by internal feedback mechanisms. Most of these mechanisms involve feedback inhibition, in which the product or result of a process stops or limits the process.

Complex animals tend to have high levels of cell specialization and internal body organization, bilateral symmetry, a front end or head with sense organs, and a body cavity.

Animals that reproduce sexually begin life as zygotes. The zygote undergoes a series of divisions to form a blastula, a hollow ball of cells. The blastula folds in on itself, forming a single opening called a blastopore. The blastopore leads to a central tube that becomes the digestive tract. A protostome is an animal whose mouth is formed from the blastopore. A deuterstome is an animal whose anus is formed from the blastopore. The anus is the opening through which wastes leave the digestive tract.

During early development, the cells of most animal embryos differentiate into three layers, called germ layers. The endoderm is the innermost germ layer; the mesoderm is the middle germ layer; and the ectoderm is the outermost germ layer.

With the exception of sponges, every kind of animal exhibits some type of body symmetry. Some animals exhibit radial symmetry, in which any number of imaginary planes can be drawn through the center, each dividing the body into equal halves. More complex animals have bilateral symmetry, in which only a single imaginary plane can divide the body into two equal halves. Animals with bilateral symmetry usually exhibit cephalization, which is the concentration of sense organs and nerve cells at the front of the body. Most animals have a body cavity, which is a fluid-filled space that lies between the digestive tract and the body wall.

26–2 Sponges

Sponges make up the phylum Porifera. Sponges are sessile, meaning that they live their entire adult lives attached to a single spot. Sponges are classified as animals because they are multicellular, are heterotrophic, have no cell walls, and contain a few specialized cells.

Sponges are asymmetrical—they have no front or back ends. Sponges have specialized cells, called choanocytes, that move a steady current of water through the body. This water enters through pores in the body wall and leaves through the osculum, a large hole at the top of the central cavity. The movement of water through the sponge provides a simple mechanism for feeding, respiration, circulation, and excretion.

Sponges are filter feeders that sift microscopic food particles from the water. Digestion is intracellular, meaning that it takes place inside cells. Sponges can reproduce either sexually or asexually. In sexual reproduction, eggs are fertilized inside the sponge's body, a process called internal fertilization. After fertilization occurs, the resulting zygote develops into a larva. A larva is an immature stage of an organism that looks different from the adult form.

Sponges provide habitats for marine animals such as snails and sea stars. Sponges also form partnerships with photosynthetic organisms.

26–3 Cnidarians

Cnidarians are soft-bodied, carnivorous animals. They have stinging tentacles arranged around their mouths. Cnidarians are the simplest animals to have body symmetry and specialized tissues. Cnidarians get their name from cnidocytes, which are stinging cells on their tentacles.

Cnidarians exhibit radial symmetry. They have a central mouth surrounded by numerous tentacles. Cnidarians typically have a life cycle that includes two different-looking stages: a polyp and a medusa. A polyp has a cylindrical body with armlike tentacles. In a polyp, the mouth points upward. A medusa has a bell-shaped body with the mouth at the bottom. Polyps are usually sessile, while medusas are motile.

A cnidarian has a gastrovascular cavity, which is a digestive chamber with one opening. Food enters and wastes leave the same opening. Digestion is extracellular, meaning that it takes place outside of cells. For gathering information from the environment, cnidarians have a nerve net. A nerve net is a loosely organized network of nerve cells that together allow cnidarians to detect stimuli. Some cnidarians have a hydrostatic skeleton. In most cnidarians, sexual reproduction takes place with external fertilization in the water. External fertilization takes place outside the female's body.

Cnidarians include jellyfishes, hydras and their relatives, and sea anemones and corals. The class Scyphozoa contains the jellyfishes. Scyphozoans live their lives primarily as medusas. The class Hydrozoa contains hydras and related animals. The polyps of most hydrozoans grow in branching colonies. The Portuguese man-of-war is a colonial hydrozoan composed of many specialized polyps. The class Anthozoa contains sea anemones and corals. Anthozoans have only the polyp stage in their life cycles. Most corals are colonial, and their polyps grow together in large numbers. As the colonies grow, they secrete an underlying skeleton of calcium carbonate (limestone). Coral colonies produce the structures called coral reefs. Many coral reefs are now suffering from the effects of human activity.

Chapter 26 Sponges and Cnidarians

Section 26–1 Introduction to the Animal Kingdom (pages 657–663)

🔑 **Key Concepts**
- What characteristics do all animals share?
- What essential functions do animals carry out?
- What are the important trends in animal evolution?

What Is an Animal? (page 657)

1. Is the following sentence true or false? The cells that make up animal bodies are eukaryotic. _____

2. What characteristics do all animals share? _____
_____

3. Complete the table about animals.

CATEGORIES OF ANIMALS

Category	Percentage of Species	Description	Examples
		Animals without backbones	
		Animals with backbones	

What Animals Do to Survive (pages 658–659)

4. What are seven essential functions that animals carry out?

a. _____   e. _____

b. _____   f. _____

c. _____   g. _____

d. _____

5. Complete the table about types of feeders.

TYPES OF FEEDERS

Type of Feeder	Description
	Feeds on plants
Carnivore	
Filter feeder	
	Feeds on decaying plant and animal material

6. Explain the difference between a parasite and a host. _____

_____

7. What does an animal do when it respires? _____

_____

8. What does the excretory system of most animals do? _____

_____

_____

9. Animals respond to events in their environment using specialized cells called

_____.

10. What are receptors, and what is their function? _____

_____

_____

11. What does it mean that an animal is motile? _____

_____

12. What enables motile animals to move around? _____

_____

_____

13. Circle the letter of the process that helps a species maintain genetic diversity.

a. asexual reproduction   c. response

b. movement   d. sexual reproduction

14. What does asexual reproduction allow animals to do? _____

_____

_____

Trends in Animal Evolution (pages 660–663)

15. What are four characteristics that complex animals tend to have?

a. _____

b. _____

c. _____

d. _____

16. How have the cells of animals changed as animals have evolved? _____

_____

_____

17. Groups of specialized cells form _____, which form organs, which

form _____.

18. After a zygote undergoes a series of divisions, it becomes a(an) _____

19. What is a protostome? _____

_____

20. What is a deuterostome? _____

_____

21. Is the following sentence true or false? Most invertebrates are deuterostomes.

_____

22. In the development of a deuterostome, when is the mouth formed? _____

_____

23. Complete the table about germ layers.

GERM LAYERS

Germ Layer	Location	Develops Into These Body Structures
	Innermost layer	
	Middle layer	
	Outermost layer	

24. Complete the table about body symmetry.

BODY SYMMETRY

Type of Symmetry	Description	Examples
	Body parts that repeat around the center	
	A single plane divides the body into two equal halves	

25. In an animal with radial symmetry, how many imaginary planes can be drawn through

the center of the animal that would divide the animal in half? _____

_____

_____

Match the term with its meaning.

Term	Meaning
_____ **26.** anterior	**a.** Upper side
_____ **27.** posterior	**b.** Back end
_____ **28.** dorsal	**c.** Front end
_____ **29.** ventral	**d.** Lower side

30. A body that is constructed of many repeated and similar parts, or segments, exhibits

_____.

31. What is cephalization? _____

_____

32. How do animals with cephalization respond differently to the environment than

animals without cephalization? _____

_____

_____

33. What is a body cavity? _____

_____

34. Why is having a body cavity important? _____

_____

_____

Reading Skill Practice

An outline can help you remember the main points of a section. Write an outline of
Section 26–1. Use the section's blue headings for the first level of your outline and
the section's green headings for the second level. Support your headings with
details from the section. Do your work on a separate sheet of paper.

Name_____ Class_____ Date_____

Section 26–2 Sponges (pages 664–667)

Key Concepts
- Why are sponges classified as animals?
- How do sponges carry out essential functions?

What Is a Sponge? (page 664)

1. Sponges are placed in the phylum _____.

2. What are pores, and where are pores on a sponge's body? _____
_____
_____

3. What does it mean that sponges are sessile? _____
_____
_____

4. Why are sponges classified as animals? _____
_____

Form and Function in Sponges (pages 664–667)

5. Is the following sentence true or false? Sponges have no tissues. _____

6. What does the movement of water through a sponge provide? _____
_____
_____

Match the body part with its description.

	Body Part	Description
_____	7. Choanocyte	a. Cell that makes spicules
_____	8. Spicule	b. Cell that uses flagella to move water through the sponge
_____	9. Osculum	c. A large hole at the top of the sponge
_____	10. Archaeocyte	d. A spike-shaped structure

11. Where does digestion take place in sponges? _____
_____

12. Circle the letter of each sentence that is true about sponges.
    a. Sponges are filter feeders.
    b. Sponges reproduce only asexually.
    c. Sponges rely on water movement to carry out body functions.
    d. Sponges do not have a nervous system.

13. How do many sponges protect themselves from predators? _____

_____

_____

14. An immature stage of an organism that looks different from the adult form is

called a(an) _____.

15. How is a sponge larva different from the adult form? _____

_____

_____

16. What are gemmules, and what is their role in sponge reproduction? _____

_____

_____

_____

_____

Ecology of Sponges (page 667)

17. Why do you think many sponges are colored green? _____

_____

_____

18. What adaptation may allow sponges to survive in a wide range of habitats?

_____

_____

_____

_____

Section 26–3 Cnidarians (pages 669–675)

Key Concepts

- What is a cnidarian?
- What two body plans exist in the cnidarian life cycle?
- What are the three groups of cnidarians?

What Is a Cnidarian? (page 669)

1. Cnidarians are members of the phylum _____.

2. What important features unite the cnidarians as a group? _____

_____

_____

3. What are cnidocytes? _____

_____

4. A poison-filled, stinging structure within a cnidocyte that contains a tightly coiled

dart is called a(an) _____.

Form and Function in Cnidarians (pages 670–672)

5. Is the following sentence true or false? Cnidarians have bilateral symmetry.

_____

6. What are the two stages in the cnidarian life cycle?

a. _____   b. _____

7. Write labels on each illustration below to name the different body parts.

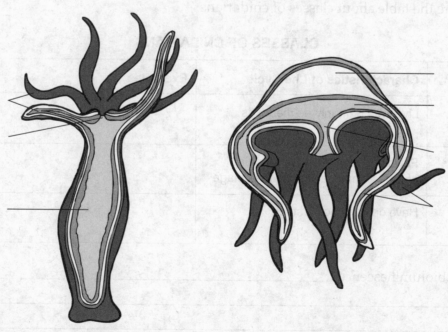

Polyp   Medusa

Match the cnidarian structure with its description.

Structure	Description
_____ **8.** Gastroderm	**a.** Digestive chamber with single opening
_____ **9.** Mesoglea	**b.** Sensory cells that help determine direction of gravity
_____ **10.** Gastrovascular cavity	
_____ **11.** Nerve net	**c.** Inner lining of the gastrovascular cavity
_____ **12.** Statocysts	**d.** Loosely organized network of nerve cells
_____ **13.** Ocelli	**e.** Layer that lies between gastroderm and epidermis
	f. Eyespots that detect light

14. Circle the letter of each sentence that is true about form and function in cnidarians.

   a. In a polyp, the mouth points downward.

   b. Materials that cannot be digested are passed out of the body through the mouth.

   c. Cnidarians respire by diffusion through their body walls.

   d. Most cnidarians reproduce sexually and asexually.

15. What does a cnidarian's hydrostatic skeleton consist of? _____

_____

16. Cnidarian polyps can reproduce asexually by _____ .

17. In the *Aurelia* life cycle, how are young medusas released? _____

_____

Groups of Cnidarians (pages 672–674)

18. Complete the table about classes of cnidarians.

CLASSES OF CNIDARIANS

Class	Characteristics of Life Cycle	Examples
	Live lives primarily as medusas	
	Polyps of most grow in branching colonies; some lack a medusa stage	
	Have only the polyp stage	

19. What is bioluminescence? _____

_____

_____

20. How do hydras differ from other cnidarians in the class Hydrozoa?

_____

_____

21. Circle the letter of each sentence that is true about corals.

    a. Corals secrete an underlying skeleton of calcium carbonate.

    b. Corals are solitary polyps that live at all depths of the ocean.

    c. Coral colonies growing near one another produce coral reefs.

    d. Most corals are colonial.

22. Is the following sentence true or false? Sea anemones are solitary polyps.

_____

23. How are coral reefs produced? _____

_____

_____

Ecology of Corals (page 675)

24. What variables determine the worldwide distribution of corals?

    a. _____

    b. _____

    c. _____

25. What do corals depend on to capture solar energy, recycle nutrients, and help lay down their skeletons? _____

_____

26. Circle the letter of each way that coral reefs can be harmed.

    a. Sediments from logging can smother corals.

    b. Overfishing can upset the ecological balance of coral reefs.

    c. Algae can remove energy from corals.

    d. Industrial pollutants can poison corals.

27. What is coral bleaching? _____

_____

_____

Chapter 26   Sponges and Cnidarians

Vocabulary Review

Completion   *Fill in the blanks with terms from Chapter 26.*

1. An animal without a backbone is called a(an) _____.

2. In sexual reproduction, the zygote undergoes a series of divisions to form a(an) _____, a hollow ball of cells.

3. A(An) _____ is an animal whose mouth is formed from the blastopore.

4. In _____ symmetry, only a single imaginary plane can divide the body into two equal halves.

5. The concentration of sense organs and nerve cells at the front end of the body is called _____.

6. A(An) _____ is an immature stage of an organism that looks different from the adult form.

7. Sponges are placed in the phylum _____.

8. A(An) _____ is a stage in the cnidarian life cycle in which the mouth points upward.

9. A digestive chamber with one opening is called a(an) _____ cavity.

Answering Questions   *In the space provided, write an answer to each question.*

10. What are the names of an animal's three germ layers? _____
_____

11. What is a body cavity? _____
_____
_____

12. What does the movement of water through a sponge provide for the sponge?
_____
_____

13. What kind of fertilization do sponges use? _____
_____

14. Which way does the mouth point in a medusa? _____
_____

15. What structures do coral colonies produce? _____
_____

Chapter 26 Sponges and Cnidarians   **Section Review 26-1**

Reviewing Key Concepts

Completion *On the lines provided, complete the following paragraph.*

Animals are _____, or composed of many cells. Those cells

                          1.

are _____, meaning that they contain a nucleus and

                    2.

organelles. Animal cells do not have _____; they

                                          3.

are surrounded only by a cell membrane. Animals are _____,

                                                        4.

because they obtain nutrients by feeding on other organisms.

Short Answer *On the lines provided, answer the following questions.*

5. Why must all living things excrete waste products? _____

   _____

6. How might sexual reproduction help a species to cope with

   environmental change? _____

   _____

7. What are some characteristics of complex animals? _____

   _____

   _____

Reviewing Key Skills

8. **Comparing and Contrasting** How is the blastopore of a protostome
   similar to that of a deuterostome? How do these blastopores differ?

   _____

   _____

   _____

9. **Comparing and Contrasting** How do the body plans of animals
   with bilateral and radial symmetry differ?

   _____

   _____

   _____

   _____

10. **Applying Concepts** What is the relationship between the degree of
    cephalization and the complexity of the animal?

    _____

    _____

    _____

Reviewing Key Concepts

Completion *On the lines provided, complete the following sentences using one of the words in parentheses.*

1. A sponge is classified as a(an) _____ (plant/animal).

2. Sponges are _____ (autotrophs/heterotrophs).

3. The cells of sponges _____ (do/do not) have cell walls.

4. Sponges contain _____ (no/some) specialized cells.

Short Answer *On the lines provided, answer the following questions.*

5. What role does the movement of water play in the essential functions of a sponge?

   _____

   _____

6. How does a sponge move water through its body?

   _____

   _____

7. Describe how a sponge obtains and digests food.

   _____

   _____

Reviewing Key Skills

8. **Comparing and Contrasting** How do sponges reproduce sexually? How does this differ from asexual reproduction?

   _____

   _____

   _____

9. **Inferring** When faced with difficult environmental conditions, sponges produce gemmules. How does this help sponges?

   _____

   _____

   _____

10. **Applying Concepts** How might the extinction of a species of sponge affect other organisms in the same kind of habitat?

    _____

    _____

    _____

Chapter 26 Sponges and Cnidarians   Section Review 26-3

Reviewing Key Concepts

Completion *On the lines provided, list five main features of cnidarians.*

1. _____
2. _____
3. _____
4. _____
5. _____

Identifying Diagrams *On the lines provided, write the stage of the cnidarian life cycle shown by each diagram.*

6. _____   7. _____

Short Answer *On the lines provided, answer the following question.*

8. What are the three groups of cnidarians?

_____

_____

Reviewing Key Skills

9. **Comparing and Contrasting** How are the functions of a statocyst and an ocellus similar? How are they different?

_____

_____

_____

10. **Inferring** What human activities or products of human activities might be responsible for a decline in coral population?

_____

_____

_____

Chapter 26 Sponges and Cnidarians   Chapter Vocabulary Review

Matching *On the lines provided, write the letter of the definition that matches each term.*

_____ **1.** invertebrate

_____ **2.** vertebrate

_____ **3.** filter feeder

_____ **4.** parasite

_____ **5.** protostome

_____ **6.** deuterostome

_____ **7.** radial symmetry

_____ **8.** bilateral symmetry

_____ **9.** cephalization

a. animal that has no backbone

b. characterized by body parts that repeat around the center of a body

c. the concentration of nerve cells and sense organs at the anterior end of the body

d. animal with a backbone

e. aquatic animal that strains tiny floating plants and animals from the water around it

f. animal whose mouth is formed from a blastopore

g. organism that lives and feeds on another organism, harming it

h. body plan in which a single, imaginary line can divide the body into two equal halves

i. animal whose anus is formed from a blastopore

Labeling Diagrams *On the lines provided, write the names of the structures that correspond to the numbers in the diagram.*

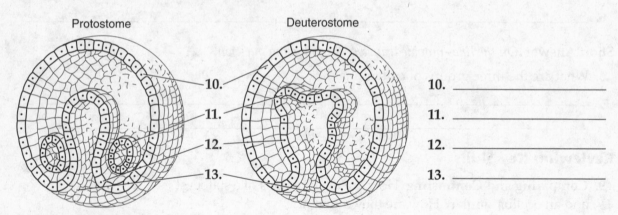

Protostome   Deuterostome

10. _____

11. _____

12. _____

13. _____

Completion *On the lines provided, complete the following sentences.*

14. The specialized cells of a sponge that produce its spike-shaped

_____ are called _____.

15. An immature stage of an organism that does not look like the adult

form is called a(an) _____.

16. A group of archaeocytes surrounded by a tough layer of spicules is

called a(an) _____.

17. Within each _____, or stinging cell, of a

cnidarian, is a(an) _____, a poison-filled, stinging structure.

Multiple Choice *On the lines provided, write the letter of the answer that best answers each question.*

_____ **18.** Which form of a cnidarian is shown in the illustration below?
 a. polyp   c. medusa
 b. archaeocyte   d. mesoglea

_____ **19.** What is the inner lining of the gastrovascular cavity in a cnidarian called?
 a. the ectoderm   c. the mesoderm
 b. the gastroderm   d. the mesoglea

_____ **20.** What lies between the gastroderm and the epidermis?
 a. the gastrovascular cavity   c. the cnidocyte
 b. the mesoglea   d. the mesoderm

_____ **21.** The digestive chamber of a cnidarian is called the
 a. nematocyst.   c. gastroderm.
 b. osculum.   d. gastrovascular cavity.

_____ **22.** What grouping of nerve cells allows a cnidarian to detect the touch of a foreign object?
 a. statocysts   c. nerve nets
 b. nematocysts   d. spicules

_____ **23.** What is the name for a group of sensory cells that helps a cnidarian determine the direction of gravity?
 a. statocysts   c. a nerve net
 b. blastulas   d. ocelli

_____ **24.** What structure allows a cnidarian to detect the absence or presence of light?
 a. a statocyst   c. an ocellus
 b. a nerve net   d. an osculum

_____ **25.** What allows cnidarian polyps to expand, shrink, and move their tentacles?
 a. a hydrostatic skeleton   c. archaeocytes
 b. choanocytes   d. internal fertilization

The Portuguese Man-of-War

The Portuguese man-of-war is a marine animal found in the open waters of the Atlantic Ocean. It is a cnidarian, a member of the phylum Cnidaria, class Hydrozoa. The Portuguese man-of-war is not just one animal; it is actually an entire colony of animals. Because the Portuguese man-of-war contains several different organisms that are functionally distinct, it is called a polymorphic colony.

The Portuguese man-of-war is striking. It looks like a blue float from above. The top portion, which can be up to 30 cm in length, has a crest that actually works as a sail. The Portuguese man-of-war is propelled by the wind at the ocean surface. Underneath the sail is a colony of individuals. The individuals, suspended from the float, have different specializations. For example, some, called gastrozooids, specialize in feeding. Others are specialized for reproduction.

Below the blue body, the colony has short tentacles and longer fishing tentacles. The fishing tentacles can be several meters in length. Cnidocytes, poisonous stinging cells, are located in the ectoderm of the tentacles and in the mouth region. Inside a cnidocyte, there is a thin, coiled thread called a nematocyst. The nematocyst responds to stimuli, such as touch or certain chemicals, by uncoiling and extending beyond the cell. Nematocysts function only once and then the cnidarian must generate new ones.

Some nematocysts contain an adhesive and entangle prey. Others penetrate the prey and inject a toxin that subdues it. After the prey is subdued, the tentacles grasp and immobilize it. The tentacles contract, bringing the prey up to the gastrozooids, which feed on it. The nematocysts of most cnidarians cannot pierce human skin. The stinging cells of the Portuguese man-of-war, however, can penetrate human skin and cause swelling, allergic reactions, and even death.

Evaluation *On the lines provided, answer the following:*

1. Describe the functions of specialized individuals in the Portuguese man-of-war.

   _____

   _____

   _____

   _____

2. Give an example of a life process that requires interaction among several parts of the Portuguese man-of-war. How does each different part contribute to the process?

   _____

   _____

   _____

   _____

Cycle Diagram

Life Cycle of the Cnidarian *Aurelia*

Use information from the chapter to complete the cycle diagram below. If there is not enough room in the cycle diagram to write your answers, write them on a separate sheet of paper.

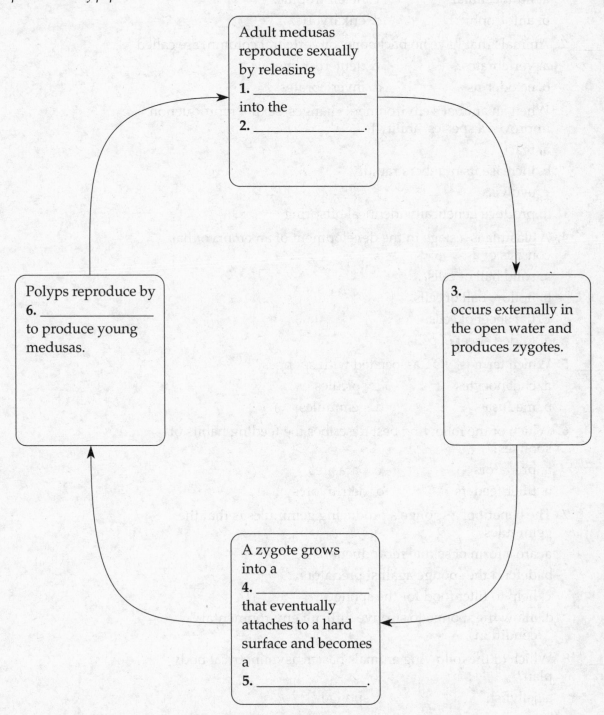

Adult medusas reproduce sexually by releasing
1. _____
into the
2. _____.

Polyps reproduce by
6. _____
to produce young medusas.

3. _____
occurs externally in the open water and produces zygotes.

A zygote grows into a
4. _____
that eventually attaches to a hard surface and becomes a
5. _____.

Multiple Choice

Write the letter that best answers the question or completes the statement on the line provided.

_____ **1.** An animal is each of the following EXCEPT
  a. multicellular.   c. heterotrophic.
  b. autotrophic.   d. eukaryotic.

_____ **2.** Animals that have no backbone, or vertebral column, are called
  a. vertebrates.   c. deuterostomes.
  b. ectoderms.   d. invertebrates.

_____ **3.** When an animal's environment changes, sexual reproduction improves a species' ability to
  a. react.
  b. increase its numbers rapidly.
  c. evolve.
  d. produce genetically identical offspring.

_____ **4.** A blastula is a stage in the development of an embryo that consists of a
  a. solid ball of cells.
  b. hollow ball of cells.
  c. flat sheet of cells.
  d. folded sheet of cells.

_____ **5.** Which term is NOT associated with sponges?
  a. choanocytes   c. spicules
  b. medusa   d. gemmules

_____ **6.** Which of the following best describes the feeding habits of sponges?
  a. predators   c. parasites
  b. filter feeders   d. detritivores

_____ **7.** The benefit of a sponge's producing gemmules is that the gemmules
  a. are a form of sexual reproduction.
  b. defend the sponge against predators.
  c. help to filter food for the sponge.
  d. allow the sponge to survive difficult environmental conditions.

_____ **8.** Which of the following animals has an asymmetrical body plan?
  a. jellyfish   c. sponge
  b. coral   d. none of the above

_____ 9. Sponges benefit some marine animals by
    a. providing a habitat.
    b. eating diseased coral.
    c. poisoning their predators.
    d. supplying them with oxygen.

_____ 10. Cnidocytes help a cnidarian survive by
    a. storing food.   c. paralyzing prey.
    b. forming colonies.   d. providing movement.

_____ 11. The body symmetry of a cnidarian is
    a. radial in the medusa stage and bilateral in the polyp stage.
    b. radial in both the medusa and polyp stages.
    c. bilateral in both the medusa and polyp stages.
    d. bilateral in the medusa stage and radial in the polyp stage.

_____ 12. In jellyfishes, the medusa stage reproduces
    a. asexually.   c. by budding.
    b. sexually.   d. by gemmules.

_____ 13. Cnidarians in the class Anthozoa are distinguished by
    a. having only colonial species.
    b. having only a polyp stage.
    c. reproducing only sexually.
    d. obtaining food only from symbionts.

_____ 14. The Portuguese man-of-war is a member of what class of cnidarian?
    a. Hydrozoa   c. Anthozoa
    b. Scyphozoa   d. Porifera

_____ 15. Coral bleaching is a serious ecological threat because it
    a. destroys the beauty of a coral reef.
    b. causes corals to die.
    c. pollutes the water.
    d. causes coral to overpopulate the area.

Completion

Complete each statement on the line provided.

16. Animals that have a backbone, or vertebral column, are called _____ .

17. The body mechanism in which the product or result of a process stops or limits the process is called _____ .

18. The opening through which wastes leave a digestive tract is the _____ .

19. The internal space of a cnidarian is called a(an) _____ .

20. In a jellyfish, the _____ stage reproduces asexually.

Short Answer

In complete sentences, write the answers to the questions on the lines provided.

21. What is the difference between a protostome and a deuterostome?

_____

_____

_____

_____

_____

22. What are the important trends in animal evolution?

_____

_____

_____

_____

23. What is cephalization? What is an advantage of that characteristic?

_____

_____

_____

_____

_____

_____

_____

24. What body form is typical of the scyphozoans? Describe this body form.

_____

_____

_____

_____

25. How are coral reefs formed?

_____

_____

_____

_____

Using Science Skills

Use the diagram below to answer the following questions on the lines provided.

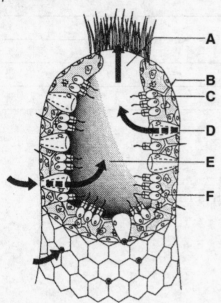

Figure 1

26. **Inferring** Why are sponges appropriately placed in the phylum Porifera?

_____

_____

_____

_____

_____

27. **Interpreting Graphics** In Figure 1, which label refers to the osculum? What is this structure's function?

_____

_____

_____

28. **Interpreting Graphics** Which label in Figure 1 represents an archaeocyte? What is the function of archaeocytes?

_____

_____

_____

29. **Applying Concepts** In Figure 1, which label represents the structure that moves a steady current of water through a sponge? What is this structure called?

_____

30. **Applying Concepts** What is the structure labeled B in Figure 1? How does this structure enable organisms within a sponge to carry out photosynthesis?

_____

_____

_____

_____

_____

Essay

Write the answer to each question in the space provided.

31. How do the three germ layers form, and what does each germ layer give rise to in the adult organism?

32. Describe an animal with bilateral symmetry. In your description, use the terms *anterior, posterior, dorsal,* and *ventral.*

33. Describe sereral advantages an animal receives from having a body cavity.

34. In sponges, how does asexual reproduction by budding differ from gemmule production?

35. Describe the feeding behavior of cnidarians.

Multiple Choice

Write the letter that best answers the question or completes the statement on the line provided.

_____ **1.** What are animals that have a backbone called?
   a. invertebrates
   b. heterotrophs
   c. vertebrates

_____ **2.** Which of the following is a trend in animal evolution as animals become more complex?
   a. having a body cavity
   b. high levels of cell specialization
   c. both a and b

_____ **3.** When an animal zygote undergoes a series of divisions to form a hollow ball of cells, it is called a(an)
   a. blastula.
   b. spicule.
   c. ectoderm.

_____ **4.** What is an animal called whose mouth is formed from the blastopore?
   a. protostome
   b. deuterstome
   c. mesoderm

_____ **5.** An animal that has distinct left and right sides shows
   a. radial symmetry.
   b. bilateral symmetry.
   c. several planes of symmetry.

_____ **6.** Unlike plants, sponges are
   a. heterotrophic.
   b. autotrophic.
   c. unicellular.

_____ **7.** What are the specialized cells that use flagella to move a steady current of water through a sponge?
   a. spicules
   b. choanocytes
   c. archaeocytes

_____ **8.** Sponges reproduce sexually through a process called
   a. cephalization.
   b. internal fertilization.
   c. radial symmetry.

_____ 9. Some sponges are green because they
      a. are more like plants than animals.
      b. filter algae out of the water for food.
      c. have photosynthetic organisms in their tissues.

_____10. Which of the following is a characteristic of cnidarians?
      a. bilateral symmetry
      b. cephalization
      c. radial symmetry

_____11. Cnidarians have two basic body types, a medusa and a(an)
      a. larva.
      b. tentacle.
      c. polyp.

_____12. The nerve cells of cnidarians make up a(an)
      a. brain.
      b. nerve net.
      c. hydrostatic skeleton.

_____13. What is a digestive chamber with one opening called?
      a. gastrovascular cavity
      b. central cavity
      c. blastula

_____14. The class Scyphozoa contains
      a. jellyfishes.
      b. hydras.
      c. corals.

_____15. Coral reefs occur in areas where there are
      a. high levels of sediment.
      b. very deep waters.
      c. high levels of light.

Completion

Complete each statement on the line provided.

16. Animals that do not have backbones are called _____ .

17. The body mechanism in which the product or result of a process stops or limits the process is called _____ inhibition.

18. All vertebrates are _____, which are animals whose anus is formed from the blastopore.

19. An immature stage of an organism that looks different from the adult form is a(an) _____.

20. The stinging cells of cnidarians are called _____.

Short Answer

In complete sentences, write the answers to the questions on the lines provided.

21. What are seven essential functions that animals carry out?

_____

_____

_____

22. What are the three germ layers that develop in most animal embryos?

_____

_____

_____

23. What is cephalization?

_____

_____

_____

24. What does the movement of water through the body provide for a sponge?

_____

_____

_____

_____

25. Describe the polyp form of cnidarians.

_____

_____

_____

_____

Using Science Skills

Use the diagram below to answer the following questions on the lines provided.

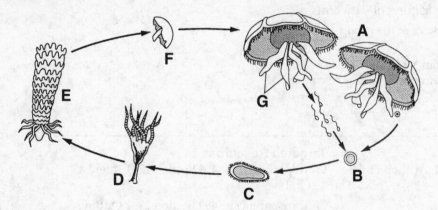

Figure 1

26. **Interpreting Graphics** In Figure 1, what letter shows a zygote, or fertilized egg?

_____

27. **Interpreting Graphics** In Figure 1, what is the structure labeled C?

_____
_____

28. **Applying Concepts** In Figure 1, is the structure labeled F produced sexually or asexually?

_____
_____

29. **Interpreting Graphics** Using Figure 1, determine which body form—polyp or medusa—reproduces sexually.

_____
_____

30. **Inferring** What evidence do you see in Figure 1 that this organism, *Aurelia*, is not a hydra?

_____
_____
_____
_____
_____
_____

LESSON PLAN 27–1 (pages 683–688)

Flatworms

Section Objectives

- **27.1.1 Describe** the defining features of flatworms.
- **27.1.2 Identify** the characteristics of the groups of flatworms.

Vocabulary acoelomate • coelom • pharynx • flame cell • ganglion • eyespot • hermaphrodite • fission • scolex • proglottid • testis

Local Standards

1 FOCUS

Vocabulary Preview
Clarify the pronunciation and derivation of the words *coelom* and *acoelomate*.

Targeted Resources
❏ Transparencies: **408** Section 27–1 Interest Grabber
❏ Transparencies: **409** Section 27–1 Outline

2 INSTRUCT

Use Visuals: Figure 27–1
Use Figure 27–1 to review form and function in flatworms. **L2**

Address Misconceptions
Address the misconception that the word *worm* only refers to an earthworm. **L1**

Build Science Skills: Designing Experiments
Small groups design an experiment to investigate how sensitive a free-living flatworm's eyespot is. **L2 L3**

Build Science Skills: Using Tables and Graphs
Students organize information in a table about groups of flatworms. **L2**

Use Visuals: Figure 27–5
Use Figure 27–5 to reinforce an understanding of the life cycle of a blood fluke. **L1 L2**

Targeted Resources
❏ Reading and Study Workbook: Section 27–1
❏ Adapted Reading and Study Workbook: Section 27–1
❏ Teaching Resources: Section Summaries 27–1, Worksheets 27–1
❏ Transparencies: **410** Life Cycle of *Schistosoma mansoni*, **411** Figure 27–3 The Anatomy of a Flatworm
❏ **NSTA** *sci*LINKS Flatworms
❏ **NSTA** *sci*LINKS Flukes

3 ASSESS

Evaluate Understanding
Call on students to explain how flatworms carry out essential functions.

Reteach
Students illustrate the life cycle of a tapeworm, using the life cycle of a fluke in Figure 27–5 as a model.

Targeted Resources
❏ Teaching Resources: Section Review 27–1
❏ *i*Text Section 27–1

LESSON PLAN 27–2 (pages 689–693)

Roundworms

Time
1 period
1/2 block

Section Objectives   Local Standards

- **27.2.1 Describe** the defining features of roundworms.
- **27.2.2 Describe** form and function in roundworms.
- **27.2.3 Identify** roundworms that are important in human disease.

Vocabulary pseudocoelom • anus

1 FOCUS

Reading Strategy
Have students copy the boldface sentences onto separate sheets of paper and then record details that support each.

Targeted Resources
❑ Transparencies: **412** Section 27–2 Interest Grabber
❑ Transparencies: **413** Section 27–2 Outline

2 INSTRUCT

Use Visuals: Figure 27–7
Use Figure 27–7 to review the body plans of flatworms and roundworms. **L2 L3**

Build Science Skills: Comparing and Contrasting
Set up a classroom display of live flatworms and roundworms. **L2**

Build Science Skills: Comparing and Contrasting
Students make a table in which they organize information about roundworms and human disease. **L2**

Use Visuals: Figure 27–10
Use Figure 27–10 to review the life cycle of an ascarid worm. **L2**

Use Visuals: Figure 27–11
Use Figure 27–11 to help students understand the significance of research on *C. elegans.* **L1**

Targeted Resources
❑ Reading and Study Workbook: Section 27–2
❑ Adapted Reading and Study Workbook: Section 27–2
❑ Teaching Resources: Section Summaries 27–2, Worksheets 27–2
❑ Transparencies: **414** Diseases Caused by Roundworms
❑ **PHSchool.com** Career links

3 ASSESS

Evaluate Understanding
Students write a comparison of flatworms and roundworms.

Reteach
Have students write a newspaper article about a person who has contracted trichinosis.

Targeted Resources
❑ Teaching Resources: Section Review 27–2
❑ **iText** Section 27–2

LESSON PLAN 27–3 (pages 694–699)

Annelids

Time
1 period
1/2 block

Section Objectives

- **27.3.1 Describe** the defining features of annelids.
- **27.3.2 Identify** the characteristics of the classes of annelids.
- **27.3.3 Describe** the ecology of annelids.

Vocabulary septum • seta • crop • gizzard
• closed circulatory system • gill • nephridium
• clitellum

Local Standards

---

1 FOCUS

Reading Strategy
Have students compare Figure 27–16 with Figure 27–3 in Section 27–1.

Targeted Resources
- ❏ Transparencies: **415** Section 27–3 Interest Grabber
- ❏ Transparencies: **416** Section 27–3 Outline
- ❏ Transparencies: **417** Compare/Contrast Table

---

2 INSTRUCT

Build Science Skills: Using Models
Students use a sock to model a tube-within-a-tube digestive tract. **L1**

Quick Lab
Students describe the structure and function of an earthworm's circulatory system. **L2 L3**

Use Visuals: Figure 27–16
Use Figure 27–16 to review form and function in annelids. **L2**

Build Science Skills: Classifying
Students classify annelids by playing a question game called Annelid Worms—Which Class? **L2**

Make Connections: Earth Science
Focus students' attention on how earthworms enrich soil and benefit plants. **L2**

Targeted Resources
- ❏ Reading and Study Workbook: Section 27–3
- ❏ Adapted Reading and Study Workbook: Section 27–3
- ❏ Transparencies: **418** Figure 27–16 The Anatomy of an Earthworm
- ❏ Teaching Resources: Section Summaries 27–3, Worksheets 27–3, Enrichment

---

3 ASSESS

Evaluate Understanding
Call on students to provide characteristics and examples of each of the classes of annelids.

Reteach
Review with students structure and function in annelids, using Figure 27–16 for reference.

Targeted Resources
- ❏ Teaching Resources: Section Review 27–3
- ❏ **ⓘText** Section 27–3

LESSON PLAN 27–4 (pages 701–708)

Mollusks

Time
2 periods
1 block

Section Objectives

- **27.4.1 Describe** the defining features of mollusks.
- **27.4.2 Describe** form and function in mollusks.
- **27.4.3 Identify** the characteristics of the three main classes of mollusks.
- **27.4.4 Describe** the ecology of mollusks.

Vocabulary trochophore • foot • mantle • shell • visceral mass • radula • siphon • open circulatory system

Local Standards

1 FOCUS

Vocabulary Preview
Caution students that the words *foot* and *mantle* have specific meanings in the context of mollusk anatomy.

Targeted Resources
❏ Transparencies: **419** Section 27–4 Interest Grabber
❏ Transparencies: **420** Section 27–4 Outline
❏ Transparencies: **421** Compare/Contrast Table

2 INSTRUCT

Use Visuals: Figure 27–21
Use Figure 27–21 to review form and function in mollusks. **L2**

Demonstration
Reinforce the understanding of a radula by showing students the woodworking tool called a rasp. **L1** **L2**

Build Science Skills: Classifying
Have students use shell guides to identify a variety of mollusk shells. **L2** **L3**

Make Connections: Physics
Use a balloon to demonstrate jet propulsion, used by octopi in movement. **L2**

Analyzing Data
Students analyze data in a graph about clamshell growth and age. **L2** **L3**

Targeted Resources
❏ Reading and Study Workbook: Section 27–4
❏ Adapted Reading and Study Workbook: Section 27–4
❏ Teaching Resources: Section Summaries 27–4, Worksheets 27–4
❏ Transparencies: **422** Figure 27–21 The Mollusk Body Plan, **423** Figure 27–23 The Anatomy of a Clam
❏ Lab Worksheets: Chapter 27 Exploration
❏ Lab Manual A: Chapter 27 Lab
❏ Lab Manual B: Chapter 27 Lab

3 ASSESS

Evaluate Understanding
Students use Figure 27–23 as a reference in labeling the drawings in Figure 27–21.

Reteach
Have students organize information in a table about the classes of mollusks.

Targeted Resources
❏ Teaching Resources: Section Review 27–4, Chapter Vocabulary Review, Graphic Organizer, Chapter 27 Tests: Levels A and B
❏ **iText** Section 27–4, Chapter 27 Assessment
❏ **PHSchool.com** Online Chapter 27 Test

Chapter 27   Worms and Mollusks

Summary

27-1 Flatworms

Flatworms make up the phylum Platyhelminthes. **Flatworms are soft, flattened worms with tissues and internal organ systems. They are the simplest animals having three germ layers, bilateral symmetry, and cephalization.** Flatworms are **acoelomates.** There is no coelom between the tissues of flatworms. A **coelom** is a fluid-filled body cavity that is lined with tissue formed by mesoderm.

All flatworms use diffusion for body functions. Some have specialized **flame cells** that remove excess water from the body. Flatworms have a digestive cavity with one opening—a mouth. Near the mouth is a muscular tube called a **pharynx,** which pumps food into the digestive cavity. The three main groups of flatworms are turbellarians, flukes, and tapeworms.

- **Turbellarians are free-living flatworms. Most live in marine or fresh water.** In free-living flatworms, several **ganglia,** or groups of nerve cells, control the nervous system. Many free-living flatworms have eyespots to detect changes in light. They reproduce both asexually (by fission) and sexually. Planarians are the most familiar species.
- **Flukes are parasitic flatworms. Most flukes infect the internal organs of their hosts.** Flukes reproduce sexually in the primary host and asexually in their intermediate host.
- **Tapeworms are long, flat, parasitic worms. They live in the intestines of their hosts.**

27-2 Roundworms

Roundworms make up the phylum Nematoda. **Roundworms are unsegmented worms that have pseudocoeloms. They also have digestive systems with two openings—a mouth and an anus.** A **pseudocoelom** is a body cavity that lies between the endoderm and mesoderm tissues. This cavity is only partly lined with mesoderm tissue.

Roundworms rely on diffusion for respiration, circulation, and excretion. The muscles and fluid in the pseudocoelom act as a hydrostatic skeleton. Roundworms reproduce sexually by internal fertilization.

Although most roundworms are free-living, some roundworms are parasitic. **Parasitic roundworms include trichinosis-causing worms, filarial worms, ascarid worms, and hookworms.**

Trichinosis is a painful disease caused by the roundworm *Trichinella*. *Trichinella* are parasites of humans, pigs, and other mammals.

Filarial worms live in the blood and lymph of birds and mammals. The filarial worms are passed from host to host by biting insects, especially mosquitoes.

Ascarid worms are parasites of humans and other animals. They cause malnutrition by absorbing digested food from the host's small intestine. They are spread by eating vegetables and other foods that are not washed properly.

Hookworm eggs develop in soil. If they find an unprotected foot, they burrow into the skin and enter the bloodstream. They suck the host's blood causing weakness and poor growth.

27–3 Annelids

The phylum Annelida includes earthworms. **Annelids are worms with segmented bodies. They have a true coelom that is lined with tissue derived from mesoderm.**

Internal walls called **septa** separate the segments that divide the annelid body. Most segments are similar to one another. A few segments, like those with eyes or antennae, are modified for special jobs. Many annelids have bristles called **setae** attached to each segment.

Annelids have complex organ systems. Many annelids use a pharynx to get their food. In earthworms, food moves through the **crop,** where it is stored. Food then moves through the **gizzard,** an organ that grinds food into smaller pieces. Annelids typically have a **closed circulatory system** in which blood is contained in a network of vessels.

Aquatic annelids may breathe through gills. A **gill** is an organ specialized for the exchange of gases in water. Most annelids reproduce sexually. Some annelids, like earthworms, are hermaphroditic. A hermaphroditic organism has both male and female reproductive organs. When eggs are ready to be fertilized, a **clitellum**—a band of thickened segments—secretes a mucous ring in which fertilization takes place.

There are three classes of annelids.

- **The oligochaetes—class Oligochaeta—are annelids that have streamlined bodies with relatively few setae. Most, including earthworms, live in soil or fresh water.**
- The class Hirudinea includes leeches. **Most leeches are external parasites. They feed on the blood and body fluids of their hosts.**
- The polychaetes—class Polychaeta—are marine annelids. **They have paired, paddlelike appendages tipped with setae.**

27–4 Mollusks

Mollusks—phylum Mollusca—are soft-bodied animals that often have an internal or external shell. Many aquatic mollusks have a free-swimming larval stage called a **trochophore.** Mollusks can be herbivores, carnivores, detritivores, or parasites. **The body plan of most mollusks has four parts.**

- The muscular **foot** is used for crawling, burrowing, or catching prey.
- The **mantle** is a thin layer of tissue that covers most of the mollusk's body.
- The **visceral mass,** made up of the internal organs, is just beneath the mantle.
- Most mollusks have a **shell.** Glands in the mantle secrete calcium carbonate (limestone) to form the shell.

Mollusks have either open or closed circulatory systems. In an **open circulatory system,** blood is pumped through vessels into large saclike spaces called sinuses. In a closed circulatory system, blood is contained in blood vessels throughout the body.

Mollusk nervous systems vary from very simple to complex. For example, the nervous systems of clams are made up of small ganglia, a few nerve cords, and simple sense organs. Octopi, however, have more complex nervous systems with well-developed brains.

There are three major classes of mollusks.

- The gastropods include pond snails, land slugs, and nudibranchs. **Gastropods are shell-less or single-shelled mollusks. They move by using a muscular foot on their ventral (lower) side.** Snails and slugs feed by using a flexible, tongue-shaped structure called a **radula.**
- The bivalves include clams, oysters, mussels, and scallops. **Bivalves have two shells held together by muscles.**
- Cephalopods include octopi, squids, cuttlefishes, and nautiluses. **Cephalopods are typically soft-bodied mollusks in which the head is attached to a single foot. The foot is divided into tentacles.** Most cephalopods have small internal shells or no shells at all. Cephalopods have many complex sense organs.

Flatworm Development

Flatworms are the simplest animals whose embryos develop three layers of cells, called germ layers. These layers, from innermost to outermost, are the endoderm, mesoderm, and ectoderm. Different parts of a flatworm develop from each germ layer.

Color the endoderm layer of the flatworm red. Color the mesoderm layer yellow. Color the ectoderm layer blue.

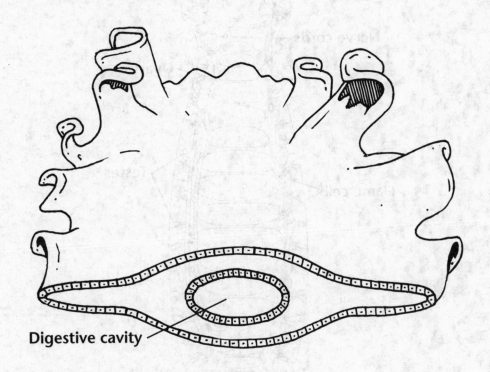

Digestive cavity

Use the diagram to answer the questions.

1. What type of tissue forms the digestive cavity?

_____

2. Which term describes a flatworm? Circle the correct answer.

   acoelomate   coelomate

3. What type of tissue forms the outermost layer of the flatworm?

_____

Flatworm Anatomy

Like other animals, flatworms have body systems for waste removal (the excretory system) and response (the nervous system).

Color the excretory system blue. Color the nervous system yellow.

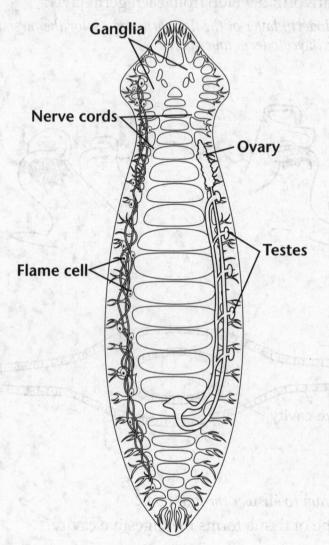

Ganglia

Nerve cords

Ovary

Testes

Flame cell

Use the diagram to answer the questions.

1. Which are parts of the nervous system? Circle the correct answer.

    ganglia   ovaries

2. What cells remove excess water and cell wastes from the flatworm?

_____

Annelid Anatomy

The earthworm shown is one example of the group of worms called annelids. Annelids are segmented worms with true coeloms.

Use the words below to label the diagram of an annelid.

body segments	crop	nephridia
clitellum	gizzard	setae

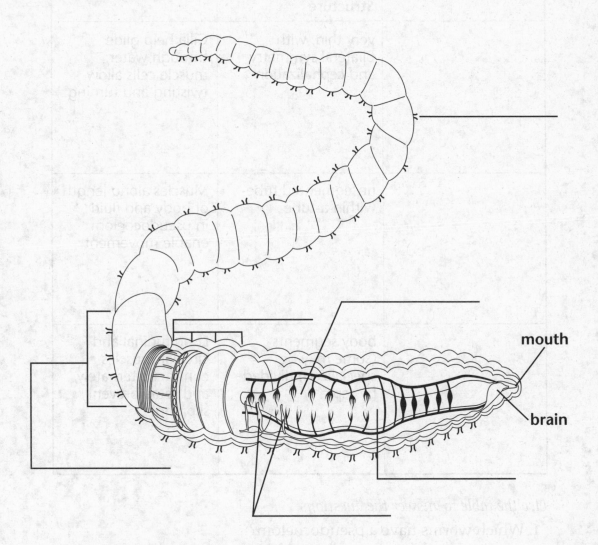

Use the diagram to answer the question.

1. Which of the structures on the diagram are part of the annelid's digestive system?

_____

Types of Worms

There are three main groups of worms: *annelids*, *flatworms*, and *roundworms*. Each group has distinctive body structures and methods of movement.

Use what you know about worms to complete the table. Write the type of worm in the first column.

Worm Type	Body Shape and Structure	Movement
	very thin, with bilateral symmetry and cephalization	Cilia help glide through water; muscle cells allow twisting and turning.
	unsegmented tube-within-a-tube	Muscles along length of body and fluid in pseudocoelom enable movement.
	body segments (some may be specialized) divided by septa	Longitudinal and circular muscles contract alternately, and setae prevent slipping.

Use the table to answer the questions.

1. Which worms have a pseudocoelom?

_____

2. Which worms have a true coelom?

_____

Mollusk Body Plans

Most mollusks have a mantle, a muscular foot, a visceral mass, and a shell. In some cases, the shell is internal. The mantle is a layer of tissue that covers most of the mollusk's body.

Choose one color for each item in the key. Fill out the key to show which colors you chose. Then color the parts of each mollusk to match your key.

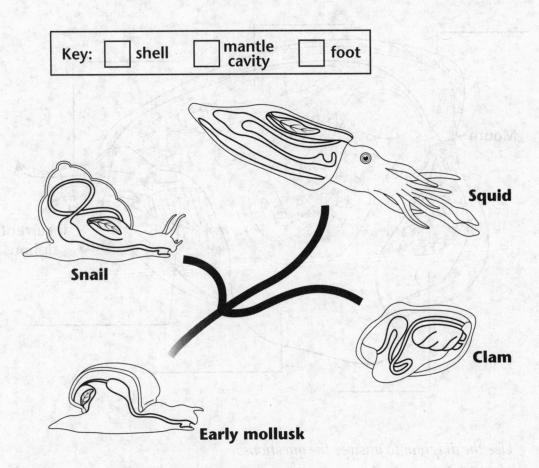

Key: ☐ shell   ☐ mantle cavity   ☐ foot

Squid

Snail

Clam

Early mollusk

Use the diagrams to answer the questions.

1. Which mollusk does not have an external shell?

_____

2. What is located just beneath the mantle in mollusks?

_____

Clam Anatomy

Use the words below to label the diagram of a clam.

excurrent siphon	gills	mantle cavity
foot	heart	shell

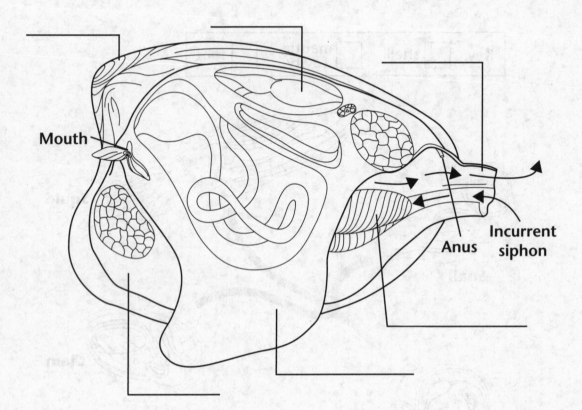

Mouth

Anus

Incurrent siphon

Use the diagram to answer the questions.

1. Which is part of the clam's respiratory system? Circle the correct answer.

shell   gills

2. Explain how the clam uses its incurrent and excurrent siphons.

_____

_____

Types of Mollusks

Use what you know to label each mollusk as a bivalve *or a* cephalopod. *The gastropods have been labeled for you.*

Mollusk	Class	Shell	Movement
Nudibranch	gastropod	none	large, muscular foot
Clam		two external	little movement; burrows in mud or sand
Nautilus		one external	regulates depth with amount of air in shell
Octopus		none	draws water into its mantle and forces it out through a siphon
Scallop		two external	flapping shells
Snail	gastropod	one external	large, muscular foot
Squid		internal supporting rod	muscular foot

Use the table to answer the questions.

1. What do the bivalves listed have in common?

_____

2. What do the gastropods listed have in common?

_____

3. A newly discovered mollusk has two shells that it flaps to move. To what group does this mollusk likely belong? Circle the correct answer.

   bivalve   cephalopod

Chapter 27   Worms and Mollusks

Vocabulary Review

Completion   *Use the words below to fill in the blanks with terms from the chapter.*

coelom	mantle	pharynx
gizzard	nephridium	proglottid

1. The thin layer of tissue that covers most of a mollusk is the

_____.

2. The _____ is the muscular tube near the mouth of a flatworm.

3. A single segment of a tapeworm's body is a

_____.

4. The _____ is a structure in annelids that grinds food.

5. The fluid-filled body cavity lined with tissue and derived from

mesoderm is the _____.

6. An organ of excretion in annelids is the _____.

Completion   *Use the words below to fill in the blanks with terms from the chapter.*

radula	trocophore
scolex	visceral mass

7. The head of an adult tapeworm is the _____.

8. The free-swimming larval stage of an aquatic mollusk is a

_____.

9. Located below the mantle, the _____ is made up of a mollusk's internal organs.

10. The tongue-shaped feed structure of snails and slugs is the

_____.

Chapter 27   Worms and Mollusks

Summary

27–1 Flatworms

The phylum Platyhelminthes consists of the flatworms. Flatworms are soft, flattened worms that have tissues and internal organ systems. They are the simplest animals to have three embryonic germ layers, bilateral symmetry, and cephalization. Flatworms are known as acoelomates, which means that there is no coelom between the tissues of flatworms. A coelom is a fluid-filled body cavity that is lined with tissue derived from mesoderm.

All flatworms rely on diffusion for some essential body functions, such as respiration, excretion, and circulation. Flatworms have a digestive cavity with a single opening, or mouth. Near the mouth is a muscular tube called a pharynx that pumps food into the digestive cavity. In free-living flatworms, several ganglia, or groups of nerve cells, control the nervous system. Many free-living flatworms have eyespots that detect changes in light. Asexual reproduction in free-living flatworms takes place by fission, in which an organism splits in two.

Turbellarians are free-living flatworms. Most live in marine or fresh water. Flukes are parasitic flatworms. Most flukes infect the internal organs of their hosts. Flukes reproduce sexually in the primary host and reproduce asexually in the intermediate host. Tapeworms are long, flat, parasitic worms that are adapted to life inside the intestines of their hosts.

27–2 Roundworms

The phylum Nematoda consists of the roundworms. Roundworms are slender, unsegmented worms. Most species are free-living. Roundworms have a body cavity that lies between the endoderm and mesoderm tissues. This body cavity is called a pseudocoelom, because it is only partially lined with mesoderm tissue.

Roundworms have a digestive tract with two openings—a mouth and an anus.

Roundworms depend on diffusion for respiration, circulation, and excretion. In roundworms, the muscles and fluid in the pseudocoelom function as a hydrostatic skeleton. Roundworms reproduce sexually by internal fertilization.

Parasitic roundworms include trichinosis-causing worms, filarial worms, ascarid worms, and hookworms. Trichinosis is a disease caused by the roundworm *Trichinella*. Adult worms live and mate in the intestines of their hosts, including humans and pigs. *Trichinella* larvae form cysts. The roundworm completes its life cycle only when another animal eats muscle tissue containing these cysts.

Filarial worms are transmitted from host to host through biting insects. Filarial worms cause elephantiasis. Ascarid worms are serious parasites of humans and other animals. Hookworms infect one quarter of the people in the world.

27–3 Annelids

The phylum Annelida consists of earthworms and other annelids. The body of an annelid is divided into segments that are separated by septa, which are internal walls. Most segments are similar to one another. Some segments may be modified to perform special functions, including segments with eyes or antennae. In many annelids, bristles called setae are attached to each segment. Annelids are worms with segmented bodies. They have a true coelom that is lined with tissue derived from mesoderm.

Annelids have complex organ systems. Many annelids get their food using a pharynx. In earthworms, food moves through the crop, where it can be stored. Then, food moves through the gizzard, where it is ground into smaller pieces. Annelids typically have a closed circulatory system, in which blood is contained in a network of blood vessels.

Aquatic annelids often breathe through gills. A gill is an organ specialized for the exchange of gases underwater. Most annelids reproduce sexually. Some annelids, including earthworms, are hermaphroditic. When eggs are ready to be fertilized, a clitellum—a band of thickened segments— secretes a mucus ring in which fertilization takes place.

There are three classes of annelids: oligochaetes, leeches, and polychaetes. The oligochaetes are annelids that typically have streamlined bodies and relatively few setae. Most oligochaetes, including earthworms, live in soil or fresh water. The class Hirudinea includes the leeches. Leeches are typically external parasites that suck the blood and body fluids of their hosts. The polychaetes are marine annelids that have paired, paddlelike appendages tipped with setae.

Earthworms mix and aerate soil. Their tunnels provide passageways for plants. Their feces enrich the soil.

27–4 Mollusks

Mollusks—phylum Mollusca—are soft-bodied animals that usually have an internal or external shell. Many mollusks share similar developmental stages. Many aquatic mollusks have a free-swimming larval stage called a trochophore.

The body plan of most mollusks has four parts. The muscular foot is used for crawling, burrowing, or catching prey. The mantle is a thin layer of tissue that covers most of the mollusk's body. The shell is made by glands in the mantle that secrete calcium carbonate (limestone). Just beneath the mantle is the visceral mass, which consists of the internal organs.

Mollusks can be herbivores, carnivores, filter feeders, detritivores, or parasites. Snails and slugs feed using a flexible, tongue-shaped structure called a radula. Mollusks have an open circulatory system, in which blood is pumped through vessels and through sinuses.

There are three major classes of mollusks. The gastropods include pond snails, land slugs, and nudibranchs. Gastropods are shell-less or single-shelled mollusks that move by using a muscular foot located on the ventral (lower) side. The bivalves include clams, oysters, mussels, and scallops. Bivalves have two shells that are held together by one of two powerful muscles. Cephalopods include octopi, squids, cuttle-fishes, and nautiluses. Cephalopods are typically soft-bodied mollusks in which the head is attached to a single foot. The foot is divided into tentacles. Most cephalopods have only small internal shells or no shells at all. Cephalopods have numerous complex sense organs.

Section 27–1 Flatworms (pages 683–688)

👄 **Key Concepts**
- What are the defining features of flatworms?
- What are the characteristics of the three groups of flatworms?

What Is a Flatworm? (page 683)

1. Flatworms make up the phylum _____.

2. What are the defining features of flatworms? _____
_____
_____

3. A fluid-filled body cavity that is lined with tissue derived from mesoderm is called
a(an) _____.

4. Why are flatworms known as acoelomates? _____

5. Is the following sentence true or false? Flatworms are the simplest animals to have
three germ layers. _____

Form and Function in Flatworms (pages 684–686)

6. Circle the letter of each sentence that is true about flatworms.

   a. Parasitic species are typically simpler in structure than free-
      living species.

   b. Free-living flatworms have organ systems for digestion,
      excretion, response, and reproduction.

   c. Free-living species probably evolved from parasitic ancestors.

   d. All flatworms rely on diffusion for some essential functions.

7. What do free-living flatworms feed on? _____
_____
_____

8. A muscular tube near the mouth at the end of the gastrovascular cavity is called
a(an) _____.

9. What is the function of the pharynx? _____
_____
_____

10. What are flame cells, and what is their function? _____
_____
_____

11. What are ganglia, and what do they do in flatworms? _____
_____
_____

12. A group of cells that can detect changes in the amount of light in a flatworm's environment is called a(an) _____.

13. How do cilia help flatworms move, and what do muscle cells allow them to do?
_____
_____
_____

14. What is a hermaphrodite? _____
_____
_____

15. What occurs during fission? _____
_____
_____

16. Is the following sentence true or false? Free-living flatworms often have complex life cycles that involve both sexual and asexual reproduction. _____

Groups of Flatworms (pages 686–688)

17. Complete the table about the main groups of flatworms.

GROUPS OF FLATWORMS

Common Name	Class	Description
	Turbellaria	
		Parasitic flatworms that infect hosts' internal organs or outside parts
	Cestoda	

18. Circle the letter of each sentence that is true of turbellarians.

    a. Most live in marine or fresh water.

    b. Most are the same color, form, and size.

    c. Most are bottom dwellers.

    d. The most familiar are the planarians.

19. How does the blood fluke *Schistosoma mansoni* infect humans? _____

_____

20. In which host do blood flukes reproduce sexually, and in which do they reproduce

asexually? _____

_____

21. On the illustration of the blood fluke's life cycle, label the primary host and the
intermediate host.

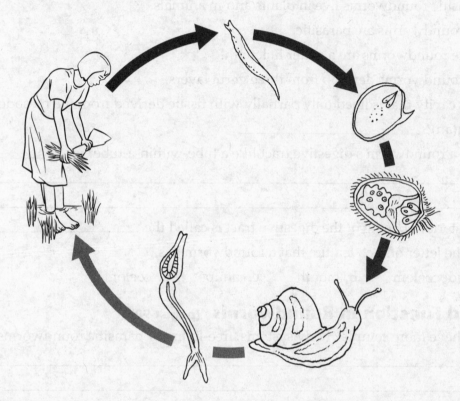

22. In what areas is schistosomiasis particularly widespread? _____

_____

_____

23. The head of an adult tapeworm is called a(an) _____.

24. What does a tapeworm use its scolex for? _____

_____

25. What are proglottids? _____

26. Sperm are produced by male reproductive organs, called _____.

27. Is the following sentence true or false? Sperm produced by a tapeworm's testes can
fertilize the eggs of the same individual. _____

Section 27–2 Roundworms (pages 689–693)

Key Concepts
- What are the defining features of roundworms?
- What roundworms are important in human disease?

What Is a Roundworm? (page 689)

1. Circle the letter of each sentence that is true about roundworms.

    a. Parasitic roundworms live in plants and in animals.

    b. All roundworms are parasitic.

    c. Some roundworms are a meter in length.

    d. All roundworms develop from three germ layers.

2. A body cavity that is lined only partially with tissue derived from the mesoderm is called a(an) _____.

3. How is a roundworm's digestive tract like a tube-within-a-tube? _____

_____

_____

4. The posterior opening of the digestive tract is called the _____.

5. Circle the letter of each feature that a roundworm has.

    a. pseudocoelom   b. mouth   c. anups   d. coelom

Form and Function in Roundworms (page 690)

6. Which have more complex body systems, free-living or parasitic roundworms?

_____

_____

7. Is the following sentence true or false? Many free-living roundworms are predators.

_____

8. Roundworms exchange gases and excrete metabolic wastes through their

_____.

9. What can roundworms' sense organs detect? _____

_____

10. Do roundworms reproduce sexually or asexually? _____

Roundworms and Human Disease (pages 690–692)

11. How do *Trichinella* roundworms cause pain in their hosts? _____

_____

_____

_____

12. Complete the table about roundworms and human disease.

DISEASE-CAUSING ROUNDWORMS

Roundworm	Disease or Condition Caused	How Disease Is Spread
Trichinella		
	Elephantiasis	
Ascarid worms		
	Weakness and poor growth	

13. What is elephantiasis? _____

_____

_____

14. Circle the letter of each sentence that is true about the life cycle of *Ascaris*.

    a. Larvae in the lungs are coughed up and swallowed.

    b. The eggs develop into larvae in the lungs.

    c. Fertilized eggs leave the host's body in feces.

    d. The host ingests *Ascaris* eggs in contaminated food or water.

15. How are ascarid worms commonly spread? _____

_____

_____

16. Where do hookworm eggs hatch and develop? _____

_____

Research on *C. elegans* (page 693)

17. Circle the letter of each sentence that is true about *C. elegans*.

    a. It is a free-living roundworm.

    b. Its DNA was the first of any multicellular animal's to be sequenced completely.

    c. It feeds on rotting vegetation.

    d. Its DNA has 30 times the number of base pairs that human DNA has.

Section 27–3 Annelids (pages 694–699)

👈 Key Concepts
- What are the defining features of annelids?
- What are the characteristics of the three classes of annelids?

Introduction (page 694)

1. Of what phylum are earthworms a member? _____

2. What evidence is there that annelids are more closely related to clams and snails than to flatworms or roundworms? _____

_____

What Is an Annelid? (page 694)

3. What is a septum? _____

_____

4. Attached to each annelid segment are bristles called _____.

5. Annelids are among the simplest animals to have a true _____.

Form and Function in Annelids (pages 695–696)

6. How is the pharynx used differently in carnivorous species than in annelids that feed on decaying vegetation? _____

_____

_____

_____

7. What is a closed circulatory system? _____

_____

_____

8. What is a gill? _____

_____

9. How do aquatic annelids respire differently than land-dwelling annelids?

_____

_____

_____

10. How do annelids keep their skins moist? _____

_____

11. What are the two major groups of body muscles in annelids called?

a. _____

b. _____

12. Marine annelids have paddlelike appendages called _____.

13. What is a clitellum, and what is its function? _____

_____

_____

14. Write labels on the illustration of the annelid for each of the features pointed to.

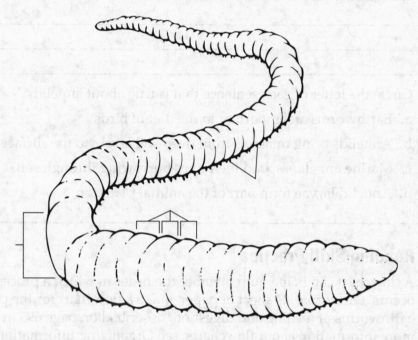

Groups of Annelids (pages 697–698)

15. Complete the table about common types of oligochaetes.

OLIGOCHAETES

Type of Oligochaete	Description	Habitat
	Long, pinkish-brown worms with few setae	
	Red, threadlike worms with few setae	

16. Circle the letter of each sentence that is true about leeches.

   a. They suck blood and body fluids from their hosts.

   b. Most live in moist, tropical habitats.

   c. They are typically external parasites.

   d. All are carnivores that feed on snails.

17. Circle the letter of each sentence that is true about polychaetes.

   a. They typically have only a few setae.

   b. They have paired, paddlelike appendages tipped with setae.

   c. They suck the blood of their host.

   d. They are marine annelids.

18. What annelids do polychaetes include? _____

_____

Ecology of Annelids (page 699)

19. How do the tunnels of earthworms affect other organisms? _____

_____

_____

_____

20. Circle the letter of each sentence that is true about annelids.

　　a. Earthworms are important to the diet of birds.

　　b. Annelids bring minerals from deep soil layers to the surface.

　　c. Marine annelids spend their lives burrowing through soil.

　　d. Annelid larvae form part of the animal plankton.

Reading Skill Practice

A flowchart can help you remember the order in which a process or series of events occurs. On a separate sheet of paper, make a flowchart for the process in earthworms of feeding and digestion, described on page 695 in your textbook. For more information about flowcharts, see Organizing Information in Appendix A of your textbook.

Section 27–4 Mollusks (pages 701–708)

🔑 **Key Concepts**

- What are the defining features of mollusks?
- What is the basic body plan of mollusks?
- What are the characteristics of the three main classes of mollusks?

What Is a Mollusk? (page 701)

1. Mollusks are members of the phylum _____.

2. Circle the letter of each sentence that is true about mollusks.

    a. They share similar developmental stages.

    b. They usually have an internal or external shell.

    c. They are the ancestors of annelids.

    d. They are soft-bodied animals.

3. What is a trochophore? _____

Form and Function in Mollusks (pages 702–704)

4. What are the four parts of the body plan of most mollusks?

    a. _____   c. _____

    b. _____   d. _____

5. What forms does the muscular mollusk foot take? _____

_____

_____

6. The thin layer of tissue that covers most of the mollusk's body is called the

    _____.

7. How is the mollusk shell made? _____

_____

8. Snails and slugs feed using a tongue-shaped structure known as a(an) _____.

9. What is a siphon? _____

_____

10. Why do land snails and slugs typically live only in moist places? _____

_____

_____

_____

11. How does an open circulatory system carry blood to all parts of a mollusk's body?

_____

_____

_____

12. A large saclike space in the body is called a(an) _____.

13. Ammonia is removed from the blood and released out of the body by tube-shaped

    _____.

14. Circle the letter of each sentence that is true about mollusk response.

    a. Clams have a simple nervous system.

    b. Octopi and their relatives have the most highly developed
    nervous system of all invertebrates.

    c. Clams have well-developed brains.

    d. Vertebrates are more intelligent than octopi.

15. Where does fertilization take place in tentacled mollusks and certain snails?

    _____

Groups of Mollusks (pages 705–707)

16. Complete the table about groups of mollusks.

GROUPS OF MOLLUSKS

Class	Common Name	Description of Shell	Examples
	Gastropods		
	Bivalves		
	Cephalopods		

17. Circle the letter of each sentence that is true about bivalves.

    a. Mussels use sticky threads to attach themselves to rocks.

    b. Some bivalves feed on material deposited in sand or mud.

    c. Clams move by flapping their shells rapidly when threatened.

    d. Scallops sting predators with recycled cnidarian nematocysts.

18. How do gastropods move? _____

_____

19. The cephalopod head is attached to a single _____.

20. What is a cephalopod's foot divided into? _____

21. What allows squids to locate a wide variety of prey? _____

_____

_____

22. The only present-day cephalopods with external shells are _____.

Ecology of Mollusks (page 708)

23. What allows mollusks to inhabit the extreme environment around deep-sea volcanic vents? _____

_____

_____

_____

24. Why can careful checks of bivalves warn public health officials of possible health problems to come? _____

_____

_____

_____

Chapter 27 Worms and Mollusks

Vocabulary Review

Crossword Puzzle *Use the clues below to fill in the spaces of the puzzle with the correct words.*

Across

3. process of asexual reproduction in free-living flatworms
6. annelid that sucks blood
7. structure in mollusks made of calcium carbonate
8. mollusk with tentacles
10. organism that has no coelom
12. type of annelid that includes the earthworm
14. thin layer of tissue that covers most of a mollusk's body
15. body cavity only partially lined with mesoderm

Down

1. soft-bodied invertebrate with an internal or external shell
2. structure in mollusks that contains the internal organs
4. marine annelid with appendages
5. fluid-filled body cavity lined with mesoderm tissue
9. structure used for respiration in mollusks
11. groups of nerve cells that control the nervous system in free-living flatworms
13. single-shelled mollusk that moves using its muscular foot

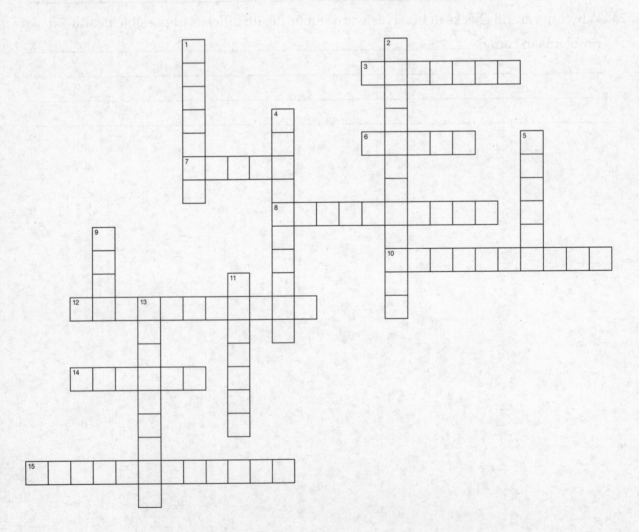

Chapter 27 Worms and Mollusks

Reviewing Key Concepts

Completion *On the lines provided, complete the following sentences.*

1. Tissues and internal _____ systems are characteristics of all flatworms.

2. Flatworms are the simplest animals to have three embryonic _____ layers.

3. Flatworms exhibit _____ symmetry.

4. Most flatworms exhibit enough _____ to have what is called a head.

Completion *On the lines provided, complete the following sentences with the appropriate group of flatworms. (Flukes, Tapeworms, or Turbellarians).*

5. _____ are free-living marine or freshwater flatworms.

6. _____ are parasitic flatworms that usually infect the internal organs of their host.

7. _____ are long, flat, parasitic worms that are adapted to life inside the intestines of their hosts.

Reviewing Key Skills

8. **Applying Concepts** How does the shape of a flatworm's body allow it to rely on diffusion for its respiration and excretion?

_____

_____

_____

_____

9. **Inferring** How does walking barefoot affect a person's chance of becoming infected with *Schistosoma*? Explain.

_____

_____

_____

_____

10. **Applying Concepts** Explain the process by which a human could become infected with tapeworms.

_____

_____

_____

_____

_____

Reviewing Key Concepts

Completion *On the lines provided, complete the following sentences.*

1. Roundworms are _____ (segmented/ unsegmented) worms.

2. The body cavity of a roundworm is described as a _____ (true coelom/pseudocoelom).

3. A roundworm's digestive system begins with the opening called the _____ (mouth/inner tube).

4. The _____ (ganglia/ anus) is the posterior opening of the digestive tract of roundworms.

Matching *On the lines provided, write the letter of the description that best matches each term on the right.*

_____ 5. trichinosis-causing worms

_____ 6. filarial worms

_____ 7. ascarid worms

_____ 8. hookworms

a. use sharp teethlike structures to enter the unprotected feet of a host

b. are transmitted from host to host through biting insects, especially mosquitoes

c. complete their life cycle only when another animal eats muscle tissue containing their cysts

d. cause malnutrition and are spread by eating foods that are not washed properly

Reviewing Key Skills

9. **Applying Concepts** How can the life cycle, and therefore the transmission, of *Trichinella* be most easily interrupted? Explain your answer.

_____

_____

Completion *Fill in the missing words to describe each of the six steps in the sequence of events in an* Ascaris *infection of a human being.*

10. Human ingests food or water containing *Ascaris* _____.

11. The eggs travel to the _____ and develop into larvae.

12. Larvae enter blood vessels and are carried to the _____.

13. The larvae are coughed up and _____.

14. Larvae develop to maturity in the _____.

15. _____ are released and leave the host in feces.

Chapter 27 Worms and Mollusks

Reviewing Key Concepts

Completion *On the lines provided, complete the following sentences.*

1. Annelids have _____ (segmented/ unsegmented) bodies.

2. Annelids have a coelom lined with _____ (ectoderm/mesoderm).

3. Annelids have a(an) _____ (open/closed) circulatory system.

4. In many annelids, bristles called _____ (setae/septa) are attached to each _____ (antenna/segment).

Short Answer *Describe the characteristics of each class of annelids.*

5. Oligochaetes

_____

_____

6. Leeches

_____

_____

7. Polychaetes

_____

_____

Reviewing Key Skills

8. **Comparing and Contrasting** How are the functions of longitudinal and circular muscles in annelids different?

_____

_____

9. **Applying Concepts** Describe the medicinal use of leeches in the past and in the present.

_____

_____

_____

10. **Applying Concepts** Describe how earthworms contribute to the health of plants.

_____

Chapter 27 Worms and Mollusks

Reviewing Key Concepts

Short Answer *On the lines provided, describe the main characteristics of mollusks and the three classes of mollusks.*

1. mollusks _____

   _____

2. gastropods _____

   _____

3. bivalves_____

   _____

4. cephalopods_____

   _____

Labeling Diagrams *On the lines provided, describe the function of each part of the mollusk body.*

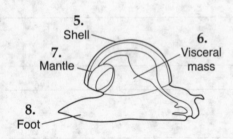

5.
Shell

7.   6.
Mantle   Visceral
                               mass

8.
Foot

5. _____

   _____

6. _____

   _____

7. _____

   _____

8. _____

   _____

Reviewing Key Skills

9. **Inferring** How does a closed circulatory system help some mollusks move faster than others?

   _____

   _____

   _____

10. **Applying Concepts** How can mollusks be used to monitor environmental conditions?

   _____

   _____

   _____

   _____

Chapter 27 Worms and Mollusks   **Chapter Vocabulary Review**

Multiple Choice *On the lines provided, write the letter of the answer that best completes the sentence or answers the question.*

_____ 1. What is the name of the fluid-filled body cavity that is lined with tissue derived from mesoderm?
   a. digestive tract   c. coelom
   b. nephridium   d. pharynx

_____ 2. Which of the following has a pharynx, flame cells, and eyespots?

   a.

   flatworm

   c.

   roundworm

   b.

   annelid

   d.

   mollusk

_____ 3. What is the term for groups of nerve cells in the head region of a flatworm?
   a. ganglia   c. seta
   b. mantles   d. visceral mass

_____ 4. Which of the following is the reproductive process in which an organism splits in two and each half grows new parts to become a complete individual?
   a. larva   c. scolex
   b. fission   d. hermaphroditism

_____ 5. An eyespot detects changes in
   a. sound.   c. temperature.
   b. light.   d. water currents.

_____ 6. What is the term for one of the segments that make up most of a tapeworm's body?
   a. a scolex   c. a proglottid
   b. a testis   d. a cyst

_____ 7. What is the term for a body cavity that is only partially lined with mesoderm?
   a. a coelom   c. a cyst
   b. a scolex   d. a pseudocoelom

_____ 8. What is the posterior opening of a roundworm called?
   a. a testis   c. a septum
   b. a gizzard   d. an anus

_____ 9. What is a bristle that is attached to a segment of an
annelid called?
a. a septum   c. a gill
b. a seta   d. a ganglion

_____ 10. What structures can be found in the digestive system
of an annelid?
a. a gullet and a crop   c. a crop and a gill
b. a crop and a gizzard   d. a gizzard and a gill

Short Answer *On the lines provided, answer the following questions.*

11. Describe how a flatworm uses its pharynx.

_____

_____

12. What are the characteristics of a hermaphrodite?

_____

_____

13. What is the function of an adult tapeworm's scolex?

_____

_____

14. Where are the septa of an annelid found?

_____

_____

15. In what kind of circulatory system does blood never leave the blood vessels?

_____

_____

16. Describe the function of nephridia.

_____

_____

17. What role does a clitellum have in reproduction in an annelid?

_____

_____

18. What is a trochophore?

_____

_____

19. What tongue-shaped structure do snails use to feed?

_____

_____

20. What tubelike structure enables an octopus to propel itself through water?

_____

_____

Chapter 27 Worms and Mollusks   **Enrichment**

Leeches

More than 300 species of annelid worms are leeches. In fresh water, leeches prey on small invertebrates such as snails and other worms. They also feed on the blood of vertebrate animals such as birds, turtles, and fishes.

Some leeches are marine animals. These leeches usually feed on the blood of fishes or sea turtles. Other leeches inhabit tropical rain forests, where vertebrates are their main prey. They attach themselves to these animals when the animals enter the water.

Leeches range in size from less than 1 cm to 30 cm long. The bodies of leeches are long and flattened. They do not have gills, but respire through their skin. Most leeches are solid brown, black, olive-green, or red. Others are spotted or striped.

All leeches have feeding structures called suckers at the head end. Suckers can vary in form and function, depending on the species of leech. One type of leech has three sharp jaws that slice through a host's skin. While the jaws work, the leech injects an anesthetic substance into its prey, so the prey feels little pain and usually does not even know the leech is there. The other type of leech has an extendible tubelike proboscis. The proboscis becomes rigid and the leech forces it into the prey's tissues.

The leeches with jaws also have an anticoagulant in their saliva called hirudin (from which their group gets its name, Hirudinea), which prevents blood clotting and dissolves existing blood clots. This compound has been the subject of much medical research. Researchers use synthetic drugs based on hirudin to prevent blood clots in heart patients and to prevent blood clots in the human brain. The proteins in leech saliva can also be used to treat cardiovascular disease. Some surgeons still use medicinal leeches to maintain the circulation in tiny blood vessels during operations.

Evaluation *On the lines provided, answer the following questions.*

1. While you are swimming in a lake, a leech uses its three sharp jaws to attach to your ankle for a meal. If you are not looking down, will you know it is there? Why or why not?

   _____

   _____

   _____

   _____

2. Why is the shape of a leech's body well suited to its method of respiration?

   _____

   _____

   _____

Chapter 27 Worms and Mollusks   **Graphic Organizer**

Concept Map

Use information from the chapter to complete the concept map below. If there is not enough room in the concept map to write your answers, write them on a separate sheet of paper.

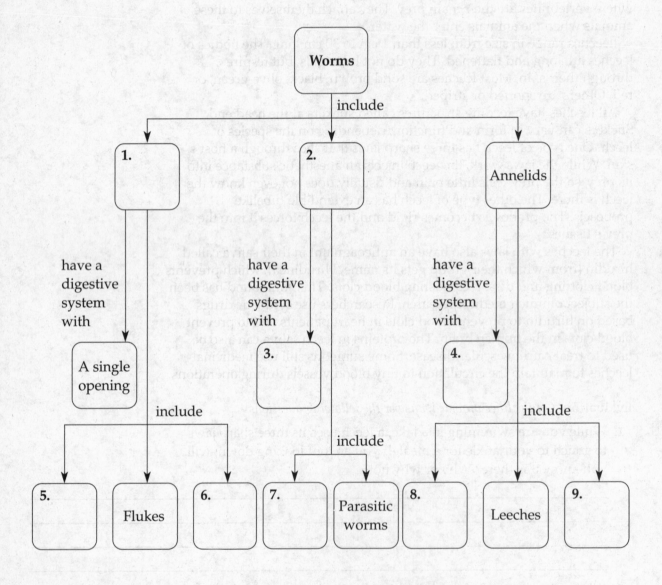

Chapter 27 Worms and Mollusks **Chapter Test A**

Multiple Choice

Write the letter that best answers the question or completes the statement on the line provided.

____ 1. Which of the following is NOT true about flatworms?

    a. They have a fluid-filled body cavity called a coelom.

    b. They are the simplest animals to have three embryonic germ layers.

    c. They are acoelomates.

    d. They are bilaterally symmetrical.

____ 2. In free-living flatworms, what organ pumps food into the digestive cavity?

    a. coelom

    b. ganglia

    c. pharynx

    d. flame cells

____ 3. Many flatworms can detect changes in the amount of light in their environment using groups of cells called

    a. flame cells.   c. ganglia.

    b. nerve cords.   d. eyespots.

____ 4. In the tapeworm, both male and female reproductive organs are contained in each mature

    a. scolex.   c. cyst.

    b. proglottid.   d. egg.

____ 5. In a pseudocoelom, mesoderm partially lines the

    a. germ layer.   c. blood vessels.

    b. body cavity.   d. pharynx.

____ 6. Which of the following is NOT true about roundworms?

    a. They have a digestive system with two openings.

    b. They have specialized tissues and organ systems.

    c. They are segmented worms.

    d. They have pseudocoeloms.

____ 7. What causes the disease called elephantiasis?

    a. flukes   c. hookworms

    b. filarial worms   d. ascarid worms

____ 8. Which of these animals has a true coelom?

    a. filarial worm   c. planarian

    b. tapeworm   d. leech

____ 9. In annelids, nitrogen-containing wastes are eliminated by

    a. clitella.   c. nephridia.

    b. parapodia.   d. gills.

____**10.** The muscular extension of a leech that penetrates the tissue of
its host is the
a. septum.   c. proboscis.
b. radula.   d. ganglion.

____**11.** The larvae of many marine annelids are ecologically
important because they
a. poison coral reefs.
b. are eaten by fishes and other marine animals.
c. feed on earthworms.
d. none of the above

____**12.** Which of the following is NOT true about mollusks?
a. They usually have an external or internal shell.
b. They are all filter feeders.
c. They are soft-bodied animals.
d. They have tube-shaped nephridia to remove ammonia from
blood.

____**13.** The tubelike structure through which water enters and leaves
a mollusk's body is the
a. sinus.   c. coelom.
b. siphon.   d. mantle cavity.

____**14.** The most active mollusks are the
a. gastropods.   c. bivalves.
b. cephalopods.   d. nudibranchs.

____**15.** Which cephalopods have external shells?
a. nautiluses   c. octopi
b. squid   d. cuttlefish

Completion

Complete each statement on the line provided.

16. A coelom is a fluid-filled body cavity that is lined with tissue derived from the
_____ .

17. A _____ is an individual organism that has both male and female
reproductive organs.

18. In an earthworm's digestive system, the _____ grinds food into small
pieces.

19. Sandworms and bloodworms are members of the class of marine annelids called
_____ .

20. A cephalopod's _____ is divided into tentacles, or arms.

Short Answer

In complete sentences, write the answers to the questions on the lines provided.

21. How can washing vegetables before you eat them help prevent the severe malnutrition associated with ascarid worms?

_____

_____

_____

_____

_____

22. Compare the body cavities of roundworms and annelids.

_____

_____

_____

_____

23. In what ways do earthworms improve soil quality?

_____

_____

_____

_____

_____

24. How do most aquatic mollusks breathe?

_____

_____

_____

_____

25. What are the three major classes of mollusks? Provide three examples of organisms in each class.

_____

_____

_____

_____

_____

Name_____ Class_____ Date _____

Using Science Skills

Use the diagram below to answer the following questions on the lines provided.

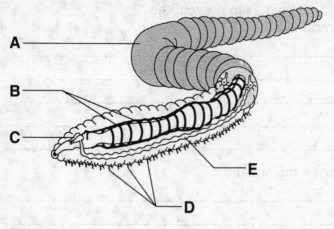

Figure 1

26. **Applying Concepts** What animal is shown in Figure 1, and in what class and phylum does it belong?

_____
_____
_____
_____

27. **Interpreting Graphics** In Figure 1, what is the structure labeled A? What is the function of this structure?

_____
_____
_____
_____

28. **Interpreting Graphics** In Figure 1, what is the structure labeled B? What is its function?

_____
_____
_____
_____

29. **Applying Concepts** Identify the structures labeled D in Figure 1. How are these structures useful to a land-dwelling animal?

_____
_____
_____
_____

30. Inferring Identify structure C in Figure 1, and infer its relationship to structure E.

_____

_____

_____

_____

Essay

Write the answer to each question in the space provided.

31. Describe the life cycle of the blood fluke.

32. Compare excretion in flatworms and annelids.

33. What is a trochophore? Why is it important in inferring evolutionary relationships?

34. How do filter-feeding bivalves obtain their food?

35. What is the difference between an open circulatory system and a closed circulatory system? Provide an example of a group that has each type of system.

Chapter 27 Worms and Mollusks

Multiple Choice

Write the letter that best answers the question or completes the statement on the line provided.

____ 1. Asexual reproduction in free-living flatworms takes place by the process known as
   a. budding.
   b. fission.
   c. fertilization.

____ 2. Some flatworms have clusters of nerve cells that control the nervous system. Each cluster is called a(an)
   a. ganglion.
   b. brain.
   c. eyespot.

____ 3. Free-living flatworms, most of which live in marine environments or fresh water, are
   a. flukes.
   b. turbellarians.
   c. tapeworms.

____ 4. An intermediate host is an organism in which a parasite
   a. reproduces asexually.
   b. reproduces sexually.
   c. causes tissue decay.

____ 5. Which of the following is a parasitic roundworm?
   a. *Trichinella*
   b. *Schistosoma*
   c. a tapeworm

____ 6. Roundworms have a digestive system
   a. with two openings.
   b. with one opening.
   c. within a true coelom.

____ 7. To move, roundworms use their
   a. proglottids.
   b. hydrostatic skeleton.
   c. tentacles.

____ 8. In earthworms, food is ground into small pieces in the
   a. crop.
   b. gizzard.
   c. pharynx.

____ **9.** The body of an annelid has

    a. a backbone.

    b. an external shell.

    c. segments.

____ **10.** A type of annelid that is an external parasite is the

    a. tapeworm.

    b. polychaete.

    c. leech.

____ **11.** The bristlelike structures on some annelids' bodies are called

    a. setae.

    b. suckers.

    c. nephridia.

____ **12.** Earthworm tunnels provide passageways for

    a. leeches.

    b. polychaetes.

    c. plant roots and water.

____ **13.** The thin layer of tissue that covers a mollusk's body is called the

    a. mantle.

    b. foot.

    c. visceral mass.

____ **14.** A pond snail is an example of a(an)

    a. gastropod.

    b. flatworm.

    c. roundworm.

____ **15.** Filter-feeding bivalves can be used to monitor the environmental health of a habitat because

    a. the bivalves reproduce rapidly in polluted water.

    b. the bivalves concentrate pollutants and microorganisms in their tissues.

    c. the bivalves live near deep-sea vents.

Completion

Complete each statement on the line provided.

16. The simplest animals to have three embryonic germ layers, bilateral symmetry, and cephalization are the soft worms called _____ .

17. Many free-living roundworms are _____ , which are animals that eat other animals.

18. Annelids have a(an) _____ circulatory system in which blood is contained in a network of blood vessels.

19. The type of embryonic tissue that lines a true coelom is called _____ .

20. The foot of most cephalopods is divided into eight or more arms called

_____ .

Short Answer

In complete sentences, write the answers to the questions on the lines provided.

21. What are the characteristics of flatworms?

_____

_____

_____

_____

22. What role do freshwater snails play in the life cycle of the blood fluke *Schistosoma?*

_____

_____

_____

_____

23. Describe the tube-within-a-tube body plan of roundworms.

_____

_____

_____

_____

24. How do hookworms infect humans?

_____

_____

_____

_____

25. What are the four parts of the body plan of most mollusks?

_____

_____

_____

_____

Using Science Skills

Use the diagram below to answer the following questions on the lines provided.

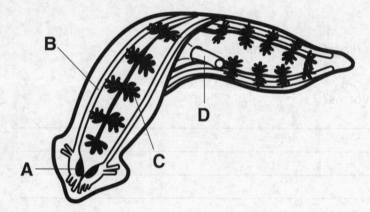

Figure 1

26. **Applying Concepts** What is the animal shown in Figure 1?

_____

_____

27. **Interpreting Graphics** Which structure shown in Figure 1 (A, B, C, or D) takes food into the animal's body cavity? What is this structure called?

_____

_____

28. **Interpreting Graphics** At the anterior end of the worm, what structures connect to nerve cords?

_____

_____

29. **Interpreting Graphics** What structure shown in Figure 1 allows the animal to sense light? What is this structure called?

_____

_____

30. **Inferring** The animal shown in Figure 1 uses diffusion to transport oxygen, nutrients, and wastes through its body. How does the body shape of the animal enable it to depend upon diffusion for transport?

_____

_____

_____

LESSON PLAN 28–1 (pages 715–719)

Introduction to the Arthropods

Time
1 period
1/2 block

Section Objectives

- **28.1.1 Identify** the defining features of arthropods.
- **28.1.2 Describe** the important trends in arthropod evolution.
- **28.1.3 Explain** growth and development in arthropods.

Vocabulary exoskeleton • chitin • appendage • tracheal tube • spiracle • book lung • Malpighian tubule • molting

Local Standards

---

1 FOCUS

Reading Strategy
Students make an outline of the section, using the blue heads for the main levels.

Targeted Resources
- ❏ Transparencies: **424** Section 28–1 Interest Grabber
- ❏ Transparencies: **425** Section 28–1 Outline
- ❏ Transparencies: **426** Concept Map

---

2 INSTRUCT

Use Visuals: Figure 28–1
Use Figure 28–1 to reinforce the meaning of the word *appendage*. **L2**

Build Science Skills: Comparing and Contrasting
Students observe a grasshopper and a crayfish. **L2** **L3**

Use Visuals: Figure 28–4
Use Figure 28–4 to review the anatomy of a representative arthropod. **L2**

Quick Lab
Students investigate whether crickets respond to odors. **L2**

Build Science Skills: Observing
Students examine a section of soil for living arthropods and molted skeletons. **L2** **L3**

Targeted Resources
- ❏ Reading and Study Workbook: Section 28–1
- ❏ Adapted Reading and Study Workbook: Section 28–1
- ❏ Teaching Resources: Section Summaries 28–1, Worksheets 28–1
- ❏ Transparencies: **427** Figure 28–4 The Anatomy of a Grasshopper
- ❏ **NSTA** *sci*LINKS Arthropods

---

3 ASSESS

Evaluate Understanding
Call on students to explain how arthropods carry out the seven essential functions.

Reteach
Students make their own drawings of the grasshopper shown in Figure 28–4.

Targeted Resources
- ❏ Teaching Resources: Section Review 28–1
- ❏ *i*Text Section 28–1

LESSON PLAN 28–2 (pages 720–725)

Groups of Arthropods

Time
2 periods
1 block

Section Objectives

- **28.2.1 Explain** how arthropods are classified.
- **28.2.2 Identify** the distinguishing features of the three subphyla of arthropods.

Vocabulary cephalothorax • thorax • abdomen • carapace • mandible • cheliped • swimmeret • chelicera • pedipalp • spinneret

Local Standards

1 FOCUS

Reading Strategy
Have students preview Figure 28–8 and Figure 28–9 and write down questions about the differences they observe.

Targeted Resources
❏ Transparencies: **428** Section 28–2 Interest Grabber
❏ Transparencies: **429** Section 28–2 Outline

2 INSTRUCT

Use Visuals: Figure 28–8
Use Figure 28–8 to review form and function in crustaceans. **L1 L2**

Build Science Skills: Observing
Students use a hand lens to observe and sketch a whole, unshelled, raw shrimp. **L2**

Use Visuals: Figure 28–9
Use Figure 28–9 to review form and function in chelicerates. **L2**

Analyzing Data
Students analyze data on a map about the incidence of Lyme disease and the ranges of the ticks that carry the disease. **L2**

Build Science Skills: Classifying
Students classify photos of uniramians as insects, centipedes, or millipedes. **L1 L2**

Targeted Resources
❏ Reading and Study Workbook: Section 28–2
❏ Adapted Reading and Study Workbook: Section 28–2
❏ Teaching Resources: Section Summaries 28–2, Worksheets 28–2
❏ Transparencies: **430** Anatomy of a Crayfish, **431** Figure 28–9 The Anatomy of a Spider
❏ **NSTA** *sci*LINKS Crustaceans

3 ASSESS

Evaluate Understanding
Call on students to explain differences in structure among groups of arthropods.

Reteach
Students organize information in a table about the three major groups of arthropods.

Targeted Resources
❏ Teaching Resources: Section Review 28–2
❏ **iText** Section 28–2

LESSON PLAN 28–3 (pages 726–733)

Insects

Time
2 periods
1 block

Section Objectives
Local Standards

- **28.3.1 Identify** the distinguishing features of insects.
- **28.3.2 Describe** two types of development in insects.
- **28.3.3 Explain** what types of insects form societies.

Vocabulary incomplete metamorphosis • nymph
• complete metamorphosis • pupa • pheromone
• society • caste

1 FOCUS

Vocabulary Preview
Help students organize the Vocabulary words by pointing out that the first four apply to the life cycle and the last three apply to behavior.

Targeted Resources
- ❑ Transparencies: **432** Section 28–3 Interest Grabber
- ❑ Transparencies: **433** Section 28–3 Outline

2 INSTRUCT

Use Visuals: Figure 28–15
Use Figure 28–15 to reinforce the anatomy of an insect. **L1 L2**

Build Science Skills: Observing
Students examine a live grasshopper and preserved insects to observe insect anatomy, especially the mouthparts. **L2 L3**

Use Visuals: Figure 28–18
Use Figure 28–18 to review the processes of incomplete metamorphosis and complete metamorphosis. **L1 L2**

Biology and History: Writing Activity
Students research and write a report about the insect-borne disease bubonic plague. **L2**

Demonstration
Demonstrate how insects communicate by mimicking the ways insects make sounds. **L1**

Targeted Resources
- ❑ Reading and Study Workbook: Section 28–3
- ❑ Adapted Reading and Study Workbook: Section 28–3
- ❑ Transparencies: **434** Insect Diversity, **435** Figure 28–18 Metamorphosis
- ❑ Teaching Resources: Section Summaries 28–3, Worksheets 28–3, Enrichment
- ❑ BioDetectives DVD: "Insect Clues: The Smallest Witnesses"
- ❑ Investigations in Forensics, Investigation 8
- ❑ Lab Worksheets: Chapter 28 Design an Experiment
- ❑ Lab Manual A: Chapter 28 Lab
- ❑ Lab Manual B: Chapter 28 Lab

3 ASSESS

Evaluate Understanding
Have students turn back to Figure 28–4 and explain what characteristics identify the grasshopper as an insect.

Reteach
Students identify the structures of an ant and explain the function of those structures.

Targeted Resources
- ❑ Teaching Resources: Section Review 28–3
- ❑ **iText** Section 28–3

LESSON PLAN 28–4 (pages 734–738)

Echinoderms

Time
1 period
1/2 block

Section Objectives   **Local Standards**

- **28.4.1 Identify** the distinguishing features of echinoderms.
- **28.4.2 Describe** the functions carried out by the water vascular system of echinoderms.
- **28.4.3 Compare** the different classes of echinoderms.

Vocabulary endoskeleton • water vascular system • madreporite • tube foot

---

1 FOCUS

Vocabulary Preview
Students skim the section to find the boldface Vocabulary words and their meanings.

Targeted Resources
❑ Transparencies: **436** Section 28–4 Interest Grabber
❑ Transparencies: **437** Section 28–4 Outline
❑ Transparencies: **438** Compare/Contrast Table

---

2 INSTRUCT

Use Visuals: Figure 28–23
Use Figure 28–23 to review form and function in echinoderms. **L1** **L2**

Demonstration
Reinforce echinoderm form and function by displaying a preserved sea star. **L2**

Build Science Skills: Observing
Students dissect a preserved sea star and make a labeled sketch of what they see. **L2** **L3**

Address Misconceptions
Address misconceptions that arise from the common names of various echinoderms. **L1** **L2**

Build Science Skills: Classifying
Students classify echinoderms. **L2**

Targeted Resources
❑ Reading and Study Workbook: Section 28–4
❑ Adapted Reading and Study Workbook: Section 28–4
❑ Teaching Resources: Section Summaries 28–4, Worksheets 28–4
❑ Transparencies: **439** Figure 28–23 The Anatomy of a Sea Star
❑ **NSTA** *sci*$_{LINKS}$ Echinoderms

---

3 ASSESS

Evaluate Understanding
Students describe the structure and function of the water vascular system.

Reteach
Students make their own labeled drawings of the sea star in Figure 28–23.

Targeted Resources
❑ Teaching Resources: Section Review 28–4, Chapter Vocabulary Review, Graphic Organizer, Chapter 28 Tests: Levels A and B
❑ **(i)Text** Section 28–4, Chapter 28 Assessment
❑ **PHSchool.com** : Online Chapter 28 Test

Chapter 28   Arthropods and Echinoderms

Summary

28–1 Introduction to the Arthropods

Crabs, spiders, and insects are in the phylum Arthropoda. **Arthropods have a segmented body, a tough exoskeleton, and jointed appendages.** An **exoskeleton** is a tough outer body covering. The exoskeleton is made from protein and the carbohydrate **chitin.** When arthropods outgrow their exoskeletons, they molt. During **molting,** an arthropod sheds its exoskeleton and makes a larger one to take its place.

   The evolution of arthropods has led to fewer body segments and highly specialized appendages for feeding, movement, and other functions. Most living arthropods have two or three body segments. All arthropods have appendages with joints (places that bend). **Appendages** are structures that extend from the body wall. Specialized appendages of living arthropods include antennae, walking legs, wings, and mouthparts. Other characteristics of arthropods are listed below.

- Arthropods can be herbivores, carnivores, or omnivores.
- Most land arthropods breathe through a network of branching **tracheal tubes** that run throughout the body. Air enters and leaves tracheal tubes through small openings on the arthropod's body called **spiracles.** Some arthropods use book lungs to breathe. **Book lungs** are organs that have layers of respiratory tissue stacked like the pages of a book. Most aquatic arthropods breathe by using gills.
- Arthropods have an open circulatory system.
- Arthropods dispose of nitrogen-containing wastes by using saclike organs called **Malpighian tubules.**
- Most arthropods have a well-developed nervous system.
- Land arthropods have internal fertilization. Aquatic arthropods can have internal or external fertilization.

28–2 Groups of Arthropods

Arthropods are classified according to the number and structure of their body segments and appendages—particularly their mouthparts.

   Crabs, shrimps, lobsters, crayfishes, and barnacles are crustaceans. **Crustaceans typically have two pairs of antennae, two or three body sections, and chewing mouthparts called mandibles.** Crustaceans with three body sections have a head, a thorax, and an abdomen. The thorax lies just behind the head and holds most of the internal organs. In crustaceans with two sections, the head and thorax are fused into a **cephalothorax.**

Chelicerates include horseshoe crabs, spiders, ticks, and scorpions. **Chelicerates have two body sections and mouthparts called *chelicerae*. Most have four pairs of walking legs.**
- Horseshoe crabs are the oldest type of living arthropods.
- Spiders, mites, ticks, and scorpions are arachnids. Spiders, the largest group of arachnids, spin strong webs by forcing liquid silk through organs that contain silk glands. Mites and ticks are often parasitic. They have specialized structures to suck fluid from their hosts. Scorpions have a stinger on their abdomen that can kill or paralyze prey.

Centipedes, millipedes, and insects are uniramians. **Uniramians have jaws, one pair of antennae, and unbranched appendages.**
- Centipedes have a few to more than 100 pairs of legs. Most body segments have one pair of legs. Centipedes are carnivores.
- Millipedes have two pairs of legs per body segment. Millipedes are detritivores.

28-3 Insects

Insects have a three-part body: a head, a thorax, and an abdomen. Three pairs of legs are attached to the thorax. A typical insect has a pair of antennae, a pair of compound eyes, and two pairs of wings. Compound eyes have many lenses that can detect small changes in color and movement. Insects use three pairs of appendages as mouthparts, including a pair of mandibles. Insect mouthparts have many shapes.

Insect growth and development usually involves metamorphosis, a process of changing shape and form.
- In **incomplete metamorphosis,** the immature insects, called **nymphs,** look much like adults. Grasshoppers go through incomplete metamorphosis.
- In **complete metamorphosis,** insects hatch into larvae that look and act nothing like adults. A larva changes into a **pupa,** the stage in which the larva changes into an adult. Bees, moths, and beetles go through complete metamorphosis.

Many insects are destructive. Termites destroy wood. Mosquitoes bite and spread disease. However, insects may also be helpful. Insects pollinate many crops.

Insects use sound, chemicals, and other signals to communicate. For example, insects can communicate using pheromones. **Pheromones** are chemical messengers that affect behavior or development in other members of the same species.

A **society** is a group of animals of the same species that work together to benefit the whole group. **Ants, bees, termites, and some of their relatives form complex societies.**

28–4 Echinoderms

Sea stars, sea urchins, and sand dollars are echinoderms. Echinoderms are marine animals. **All have spiny skin, a water vascular system, and tube feet. They also have an endoskeleton, or internal skeleton. Most adult echinoderms show five-part radial symmetry.** Echinoderms are deuterostomes. This suggests that echinoderms and vertebrates are closely related. In most echinoderms, waste is released as feces through the anus. Echinoderms reproduce by external fertilization.

Echinoderms have a system of internal tubes called a **water vascular system. The water vascular system is filled with fluid. It carries out vital body functions, including respiration, circulation, and movement.** This system opens to the outside through a structure called a **madreporite.** In sea stars, the madreporite connects to a ring canal. From the ring canal, five radial canals extend along body segments. Attached to each are hundreds of **tube feet.** A tube foot works much like a suction cup. Most echinoderms move by using their tube feet. Tube feet provide the main surface for respiration in many species of echinoderms. The water vascular system also functions to circulate materials through the echinoderm. Oxygen, food, and wastes are carried by the water vascular system.

Echinoderms have several feeding methods. For example, some use their water vascular system to capture floating plankton. Others feed on organisms such as clams and mussels. In most echinoderms, waste is released as feces through the anus. The nervous systems of echinoderms are simple. Most are made up of a nerve ring, radial nerves, and sensory cells. Echinoderms reproduce by external fertilization.

Classes of echinoderms include: sea urchins and sand dollars, brittle stars, sea cucumbers, sea stars, and sea lilies and feather stars.

Arthropod Anatomy

The grasshopper shown is one example of an arthropod. The organs and body structures shown are common to many arthropods.

Use the words below to label the diagram. Some structures have been labeled for you.

brain	Malpighian tubules	tracheal tubes
compound eye	spiracles	

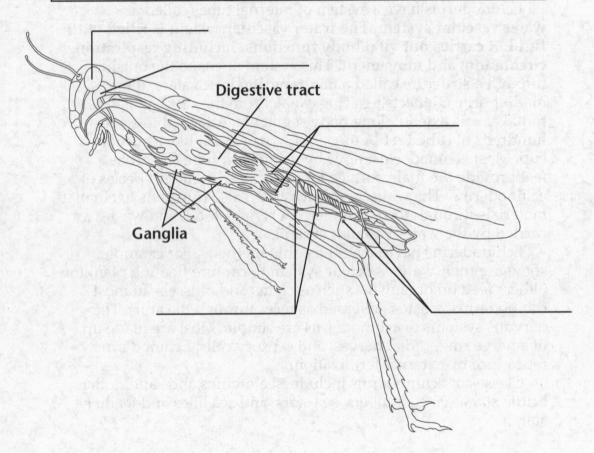

Digestive tract

Ganglia

Use the diagram to answer the questions.

1. Which is part of the excretory system? Circle the correct answer.

   compound eye   Malpighian tubules

2. Which structures shown are part of the respiratory system?

   _____

Crustacean Anatomy

The crayfish shown is one example of a crustacean. Most crustaceans have similar body organization and body structures.

Color the tail section red. Color the abdomen blue. Color the cephalothorax yellow. Then use the words below to label the diagram.

carapace	cheliped	mandible	swimmerets

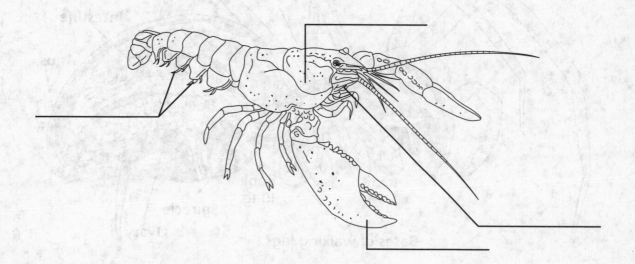

Use the diagram to answer the questions.

1. In what section is the carapace located? Circle the correct answer.

abdomen   cephalothorax

2. What structure does the crustacean use to catch and crush food?

_____

3. For what does the crustacean shown use its swimmerets?

_____

4. What does the crustacean shown use to bite and grind food? Circle the correct answer.

mandible   abdomen

Spider Anatomy

Follow the prompts to identify the spider's body systems. The circulatory system is shaded for you.
- Color the structures in the digestive system green.
- Color the structures in the respiratory system blue.
- Color the structures in the reproductive system red.

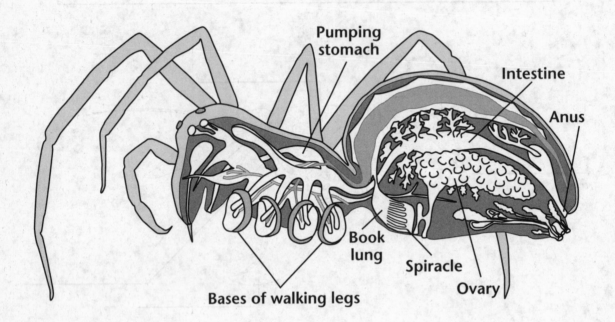

Use the diagram to answer the questions.

1. Which organ is part of the respiratory system? Circle the correct answer.

   spinneret   spiracle

2. What does a spider use its chelicerae for?

   _____

3. What labeled organs does a spider use for digestion?

   _____

4. Can spiders chew their prey? Explain.

   _____

   _____

Most Animals Are Insects

Ninety-six percent of all animal species living today are inverte-brates. Most of these animals are insects.

Use the circle graph to make a bar graph showing the percentage of all living animal species that are members of each group.

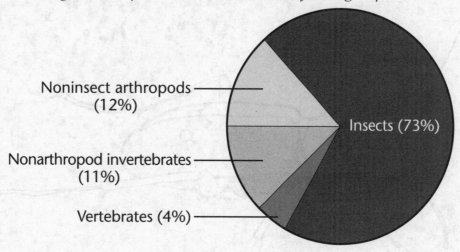

Noninsect arthropods (12%)

Nonarthropod invertebrates (11%)

Vertebrates (4%)

Insects (73%)

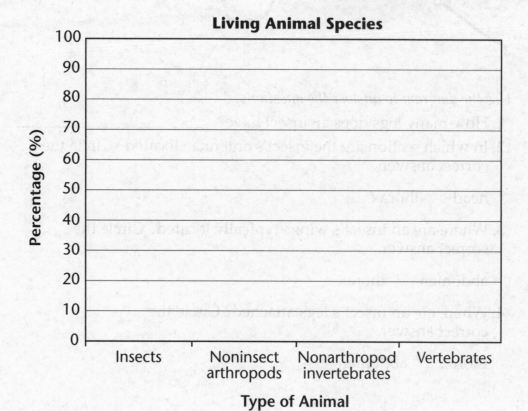

Living Animal Species

Percentage (%)

Insects   Noninsect arthropods   Nonarthropod invertebrates   Vertebrates

Type of Animal

Use the graphs to answer the question.

1. Which group contains the largest percentage of all living animal species?

_____

Insects

Insects have three body sections: the abdomen, the head, and the thorax.

Color the insect's abdomen yellow. Color the head red. Color the thorax blue.

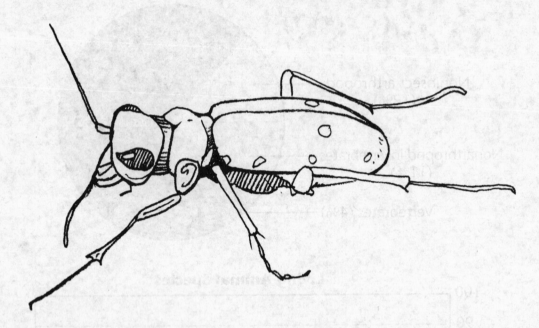

Use the diagram to answer the questions.

1. How many legs does an insect have? _____

2. In which section are the insect's antennae located? Circle the correct answer.

   head   thorax

3. Where are an insect's wings typically located? Circle the correct answer.

   abdomen   thorax

4. Where are an insect's legs attached? Circle the correct answer.

   thorax   abdomen

Complete and Incomplete Metamorphosis

As insects develop, they usually go through either complete or incomplete metamorphosis. Metamorphosis is the process of changing shape and form.

Label each stage as adult, eggs, larva, nymph, *or* pupa. *You may use labels more than once.*

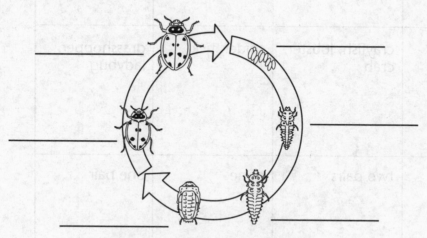

Complete Metamorphosis

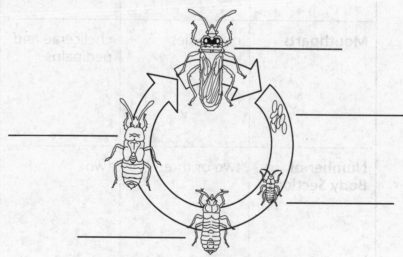

Incomplete Metamorphosis

Use the diagrams to answer the question.

1. What is the difference between complete and incomplete metamorphosis?

_____

_____

_____

Types of Arthropods

The table lists characteristics of the three types of arthropods. Use what you know about the groups of arthropods to fill in the column headings. Identify each group as crustaceans, chelicerates, *or* uniramians.

Arthropod Type			
Example	crayfish, lobster, crab	spider, tick	grasshopper, ladybug
Antennae	two pairs	none	one pair
Mouthparts	mandibles	chelicerae and pedipalps	jaws
Number of Body Sections	two or three	two	varied; insects have three

1. A scorpion has chelicerae and pedipalps. To which group does it belong?

_____

2. In a crustacean with two body sections, what are the two sections called?

_____

Echinoderm Anatomy

The sea star shown here is one example of an echinoderm. Its body structures are common to many echinoderms.

Use the words below to label the diagram.

eyespot	radial canal	stomach
madreporite	ring canal	tube foot

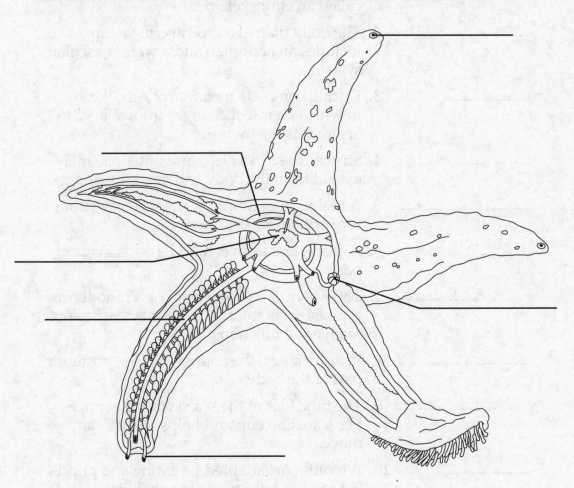

Use the diagram to answer the questions.

1. Which structures are part of the water vascular system?

_____

_____

2. What kind of skeleton do echinoderms have? Circle the correct answer.

external   internal

Chapter 28   Arthropods and Echinoderms

Vocabulary Review

True or False   *If the statement is true, write* true. *If it is false, write* false.

_____ **1.** Arthropods have a tough outer covering called an endoskeleton.

_____ **2.** The body plan of a typical crustacean includes an abdomen and a water vascular system.

_____ **3.** During complete metamorphosis, the stage in which an insect changes from a larva to an adult is the nymph.

_____ **4.** Structures such as legs and antennae that extend from the body wall are appendages.

_____ **5.** A Malpighian tubule is an excretory structure of arthropods.

_____ **6.** A characteristic of echinoderms is a carapace.

_____ **7.** The water-vascular system of echinoderms is a system of internal tubes that carries out many vital functions.

_____ **8.** In arthropods, the abdomen is the posterior part of the body.

_____ **9.** The tube foot of the sea star works much like a suction cup and helps the sea star move.

_____ **10.** A mouthpart adapted for biting and grinding food in arthropods is a cheliped.

_____ **11.** During metamorphosis, arthropods shed their entire exoskeleton and make a larger one to take its place.

Chapter 28   Arthropods and Echinoderms

Summary

28–1 Introduction to the Arthropods

Phylum Arthropoda includes animals such as crabs, spiders, and insects. Arthropods have a segmented body, a tough exoskeleton, and jointed appendages. An exoskeleton is an external body covering. An arthropod exoskeleton is made from protein and a carbohydrate called chitin. All arthropods have jointed appendages. Appendages are structures such as legs and antennae that extend from the body wall.

The evolution of arthropods—by natural selection and other processes—has led to fewer body segments and highly specialized appendages for feeding, movement, and other functions. Most living arthropods have only two or three segments. Living arthropods have specialized appendages such as antennae, walking legs, wings, and mouthparts.

Arthropods include herbivores, carnivores, and omnivores. Most terrestrial arthropods breathe through a network of branching tracheal tubes that extend throughout the body. Air enters and leaves the tracheal tubes through small openings called spiracles. Other terrestrial arthropods, such as spiders, respire using book lungs. Most aquatic arthropods have gills. Arthropods have an open circulatory system. Most terrestrial arthropods dispose of nitrogen-containing wastes using saclike organs called Malpighian tubules. Terrestrial arthropods have internal fertilization. Aquatic arthropods have internal or external fertilization.

When arthropods outgrow their exoskeltons, they undergo periods of molting. During molting, an arthropod sheds its entire exoskeleton and manufactures a larger one to take its place.

28–2 Groups of Arthropods

Arthropods are classified based on the number and structure of their body segments and appendages—particularly their mouthparts.

Crustaceans—subphylum Crustacea—include crabs, shrimps, lobsters, crayfishes, and barnacles. Crustaceans typically have two pairs of antennae, two or three body sections, and chewing mouthparts called mandibles. Crustaceans with three body sections have a head, a thorax, and an abdomen. The thorax lies just behind the head and houses most of the internal organs. In crustaceans with two sections, the head and thorax are fused, forming a cephalothorax.

Chelicerates—subphylum Chelicerata—include horseshoe crabs, spiders, ticks, and scorpions. Chelicerates have mouthparts called chelicerae and two body sections. Nearly all chelicerates have four pairs of walking legs. Chelicerates are divided into two main classes—Merostomata and Arachnida. Class Merostomata includes horseshoe crabs. Horseshoe crabs are the oldest living arthropods. Class Arachnida includes spiders, mites, ticks, and scorpions. Spiders are the largest group of arachnids. Spiders spin strong webs by forcing liquid silk through spinnerets, organs that contain silk glands.

Uniramians—subphylum Uniramia—include centipedes, millipedes, and insects. Uniramians have jaws, one pair of antennae, and unbranched appendages. Centipedes have a few to more than 100 pairs of legs. Most body segments have one pair of legs each. Centipedes are carnivores. Millipedes have two, not one, pairs of legs per segment. Millipedes feed on dead or decaying plant material.

28–3 Insects

Insects have a body divided into three parts—head, thorax, and abdomen. Three pairs of legs are attached to the thorax. A typical insect has a pair of antennae, a pair of compound eyes, and two pairs of wings. Compound eyes are made of many lenses, and they detect minute changes in color and movement.

Insects have three pairs of appendages used as mouthparts, including a pair of mandibles. Insect mouthparts are a variety of shapes.

The growth and development of insects usually involve metamorphosis, which is a process of changing shape and form. In incomplete metamorphosis, the immature forms of insects look very much like adults. The immature forms are called nymphs. Nymphs gradually acquire adult structures, such as wings, and functional sex organs. Insects such as bees, moths, and beetles undergo complete metamorphosis. These insects hatch into larvae that look and act nothing like adults. A larva changes into a pupa, the stage in which an insect changes from larva to adult.

Insects are known for their destructive effects. Termites destroy wood, and mosquitoes bite humans. Yet, insects are also beneficial to humans. For example, insects pollinate many crops.

Insects communicate using sound, chemical, and other types of signals. Pheromones are specific chemical messengers that affect behavior or development in other individuals of the same species.

Ants, bees, termites, and some of their relatives form complex associations called societies. A society is a group of animals of the same species that work together for the benefit of the whole group.

28–4 Echinoderms

Phylum Echinodermata consists of animals such as sea stars, sea urchins, and sand dollars. Echinoderms are characterized by spiny skin, a water vascular system, and suction-cuplike structures called tube feet. Echinoderms have an endoskeleton, which is an internal skeleton. Most adult echinoderms exhibit five-part radial symmetry. Echinoderm larvae exhibit bilateral symmetry. Echinoderms are deuterostomes—an indication that echinoderms and vertebrates are closely related.

Echinoderms have a system of internal tubes called a water vascular system. The water vascular system is filled with fluid. It carries out many essential body functions in echinoderms, including respiration, circulation, and movement. It opens to the outside through a sievelike structure called a madreporite. In sea stars, the madreporite connects to a ring canal. From the ring canal, five radial canals extend along body segments. Attached to each radial canal are hundreds of tube feet. A tube foot is a structure that operates much like a suction cup. In most echinoderms, waste is released as feces through the anus. Most echinoderms move using their tube feet. Echinoderms reproduce by external fertilization.

Classes of echinoderms include sea urchins and sand dollars, brittle stars, sea cucumbers, sea stars, and sea lilies and feather stars. Echinoderms are common in a variety of marine habitats. Sea urchins help control the distribution of algae and other forms of marine life. Sea stars are important predators that help control the numbers of clams and corals.

Section 28–1 Introduction to the Arthropods
(pages 715–719)

🔑 Key Concepts
- What are the main features of arthropods?
- What are the important trends in arthropod evolution?
- What happens when an arthropod outgrows its exoskeleton?

What Is an Arthropod? (page 715)

1. What is the basic body plan of all arthropods? _____

_____

_____

2. A tough body wall that protects and supports the body of arthropods is called a(an)

_____.

3. What is chitin? _____

_____

_____

4. Circle the letter of each sentence that is true about arthropod exoskeletons.

    a. The exoskeletons of many land-dwelling species have a waxy covering.

    b. All arthropod exoskeletons are the same shape.

    c. Lobster exoskeletons cannot be crushed by hand.

    d. An exoskeleton is an external covering.

5. What are appendages? _____

_____

_____

6. Is the following sentence true or false? The appendages of arthropods are jointed.

_____

Evolution of Arthropods (page 716)

7. Where did the first arthropods appear more than 600 million years ago?

_____

8. What are two ways in which arthropods have evolved since they first appeared?

    a. _____

    b. _____

9. Circle the letter of each sentence that is true about arthropod evolution.

   a. Most primitive arthropods had only one or two body segments.

   b. Arthropod appendages evolved into different forms.

   c. The early body plan was modified gradually.

   d. Appendages of living arthropods include wings, flippers, and mouthparts.

Form and Function in Arthropods (pages 716–719)

10. Is the following sentence true or false? Arthropods include herbivores, carnivores, and omnivores. _____

Match the arthropod structure with its description.

Structure	Description
_____ **11.** Tracheal tubes	**a.** Saclike organs that extract wastes from the blood and add them to feces
_____ **12.** Spiracles	**b.** Network of branching tubes through which arthropods breathe
_____ **13.** Book lungs	
_____ **14.** Book gills	**c.** Organs through which horseshoe crabs respire
_____ **15.** Malpighian tubules	**d.** Layers of respiratory tissue stacked like the pages of a book through which spiders respire
	e. Small openings on the side of the body through which air enters and leaves tracheal tubes

16. Complete the concept map about arthropod respiration.

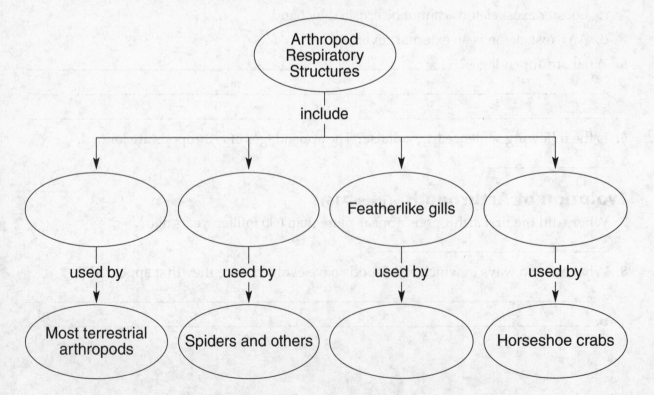

17. Circle the letter of each sentence that is true about the response to the environment by arthropods.

   a. Most arthropods have sophisticated sense organs.

   b. All arthropods have a brain.

   c. Ganglia along a ventral nerve cord coordinate the movements of individual legs.

   d. Very few arthropods have a well-developed nervous system.

18. How do aquatic arthropods carry out excretion? _____

_____

_____

19. How do arthropods move? _____

_____

20. Circle the letter of each sentence that is true about arthropod reproduction.

   a. Aquatic arthropods have only internal fertilization.

   b. In some species, males have an organ that places sperm inside females.

   c. Terrestrial arthropods may have internal or external fertilization.

   d. In some aquatic species, males shed sperm around eggs released into the environment.

Growth and Development in Arthropods (page 719)

21. When do arthropods undergo periods of molting? _____

_____

22. What occurs in arthropods during molting? _____

_____

_____

Section 28–2 Groups of Arthropods
(pages 720–725)

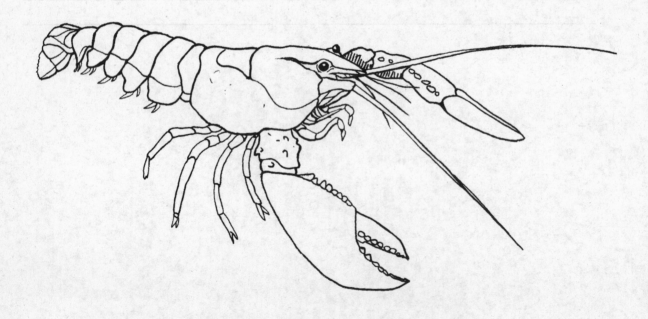 Key Concepts
- How are arthropods classified?
- What are the distinguishing features of the three major groups of arthropods?

Introduction (page 720)

1. What characteristics do biologists use to classify arthropods? _____
_____
_____

2. What are the three major groups of arthropods?

   a. _____
   b. _____
   c. _____

Crustaceans (pages 720–721)

3. Circle the letter of each description of structures that crustaceans typically have.

   a. two pairs of branched antennae

   b. four or five body sections

   c. chewing mouthparts called mandibles

   d. two or three body sections

4. Label the two body sections of a typical crustacean.

5. The largest group of crustaceans is the _____.

6. Complete the table about crustacean body parts.

CRUSTACEAN BODY PARTS

Body Part	Description
Thorax	
	Fusion of the head with the thorax
Abdomen	
	The part of the exoskeleton that covers the cephalothorax
Mandible	
	First pair of legs in decapods, which bear large claws
Swimmerets	

7. Circle the letter of each sentence that is true about barnacles.

   a. They are sessile.

   b. They have an outer, shell-like covering.

   c. They move backward by snapping a tail.

   d. They attach themselves to rocks and marine animals.

Spiders and Their Relatives (pages 722–724)

8. Horseshoe crabs, spiders, ticks, and scorpions are grouped as _____.

9. Circle the letter of each description of structures that chelicerates have.

   a. four or five pairs of legs

   b. three or four body sections

   c. two pairs of branched antennae

   d. mouthparts called chelicerae

10. What is the function of the chelicerae? _____

    _____

    _____

11. The appendages near the mouth that are usually modified to grab prey are called

    _____.

12. How do spiders respire? _____

    _____

13. What arthropods do arachnids include? _____

_____

14. How are horseshoe crabs like and unlike crabs? _____

_____

_____

15. Why must spiders liquefy their food to swallow it? _____

_____

16. Circle the letter of each sentence that is true about spiders and silk.

    a. Spiders spin silk into cocoons for eggs.

    b. Spinning webs seems to be a programmed behavior.

    c. Spinnerets are organs that contain silk glands.

    d. Tarantulas cannot produce silk.

17. Is the following sentence true or false? Mites and ticks are often parasitic.

    _____

18. Scorpions have pedipalps that are enlarged into _____.

19. What do ticks transmit that cause Rocky Mountain spotted fever and Lyme disease?

_____

_____

Insects and Their Relatives (page 725)

20. Centipedes, millipedes, and insects are all grouped as _____.

21. Circle the letter of each description of structures that uniramians have.

    a. one pair of antennae

    b. unbranched appendages

    c. mouthparts called chelicerae

    d. jaws

22. Why are centipedes restricted to moist or humid areas? _____

_____

_____

23. How many pairs of legs does each body segment of most centipedes have? _____

_____

_____

24. How many pairs per segment do millipedes have?

_____

_____

Section 28–3 Insects (pages 726–733)

Key Concepts
- What are the distinguishing features of insects?
- What two types of development can insects undergo?
- What types of insects form societies?

Introduction (page 726)

1. What are three characteristics of insects that have contributed to their evolutionary success?

   a. _____

   b. _____

   c. _____

What Is an Insect? (pages 727–729)

2. Label the three body parts of an insect.

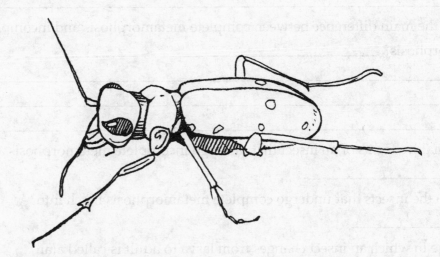

3. How many pairs of legs does an insect have, and where are they attached?

   _____

4. Circle the letter of each sentence that is true about a typical insect.

   a. It has tracheal tubes used for respiration.

   b. It has a pair of compound eyes on the head.

   c. It has two pairs of wings on the abdomen.

   d. It has a pair of antennae on the head.

5. What is the multiple-lens structure of the compound eye better at detecting than the human eye? _____

6. Where do insects have chemical receptors for taste and smell? _____

   _____

7. Is the following sentence true or false? Many insects have well-developed ears.
   _____

8. Why do insect mouthparts take on a variety of shapes? _____
   _____
   _____

9. How many pairs of wings does a flying insect typically have, and what are they
   made of? _____
   _____
   _____

10. What has the evolution of flight allowed insects to do? _____
    _____
    _____
    _____

11. What is metamorphosis? _____
    _____

12. What is the main difference between complete metamorphosis and incomplete
    metamorphosis? _____
    _____
    _____
    _____

13. The immature forms of an insect that undergo incomplete metamorphosis are
    called _____.

14. What do the insects that undergo complete metamorphosis hatch into?
    _____

15. The stage in which an insect changes from larva to adult is called a(an)
    _____.

16. Circle the letter of each sentence that is true about complete metamorphosis.
    a. The nymphs gradually acquire adult structures.
    b. During the pupal stage, the body is completely remodeled
       inside and out.
    c. The larva molts a few times but changes little in appearance.
    d. The adult that emerges seems like a completely different
       animal from the larva.

Insects and Humans (page 730)

17. Is the following sentence true or false? Only male mosquitoes bite humans and other animals to get a blood meal. _____

18. How do insects contribute beneficially to agriculture? _____

_____

_____

_____

Insect Communication (page 731)

19. Circle the letter of each sentence that is true about insect communication.

a. To attract females, male crickets chirp.

b. Much of an insect's communication involves finding a mate.

c. Insects communicate using visual signals.

d. Fireflies use sound cues to communicate with potential mates.

20. What are pheromones? _____

_____

_____

Insect Societies (pages 732–733)

21. What is a society? _____

_____

_____

22. Circle the letter of each sentence that is true about castes.

a. Each caste has a body form specialized for its role.

b. Most insect societies have multiple queens.

c. Groups of individuals in a society are specialized to perform particular tasks.

d. The queen is typically the largest individual in the colony.

23. What does a honeybee's round dance tell the other bees? _____

_____

Reading Skill Practice

By looking carefully at illustrations in textbooks, you can help yourself understand better what you have read. Look carefully at Figure 28–16 on page 728 in your textbook. What important idea do these illustrations communicate? Do your work on a separate sheet of paper.

Section 28–4 Echinoderms (pages 734–738)

👌 **Key Concepts**
- What are the distinguishing features of echinoderms?
- What functions are carried out by the water vascular system of echinoderms?
- What are the different classes of echinoderms?

Introduction (page 734)

1. An internal skeleton is called a(an) _____.

2. What forms an echinoderm's endoskeleton? _____
_____

3. In what environment do all echinoderms live? _____

What Is an Echinoderm? (page 734)

4. Is the following sentence true or false? The bodies of most echinoderms are
two-sided. _____

5. What are five features that characterize echinoderms?

 a. _____   d. _____

 b. _____   e. _____

 c. _____

6. What characteristic of echinoderms indicates that they are closely related to
vertebrates? _____

Form and Function in Echinoderms (pages 735–736)

7. What functions does the water vascular system carry out in echinoderms?
_____

8. The water vascular system opens to the outside through a sievelike structure called
a(an) _____.

9. What is a tube foot? _____

10. Is the following sentence true or false? Sea stars usually feed on mollusks.

_____

11. In most echinoderms, how are solid wastes released? _____
_____

12. What is the structure of the nervous system in most echinoderms? _____
_____
_____

13. What do most echinoderms use to move? _____

14. Is the following sentence true or false? Echinoderms reproduce by internal
fertilization. _____

Groups of Echinoderms (pages 737–738)

15. Complete the table about groups of echinoderms.

GROUPS OF ECHINODERMS

Group	Description of Feeding	Description of Body
	Many are detritivores or grazers	Disk-shaped
Sea cucumbers		Look like warty, moving pickles
Sea stars	Carnivores	
		Long, feathery arms and attached to the ocean bottom by a stalk

16. How do sand dollars defend themselves? _____

_____

17. When a brittle star is attacked, it sheds one or more arms. How does this help the

echinoderm? _____

_____

18. Where are most sea cucumbers found? _____

19. What happens if a sea star is pulled into pieces? _____

_____

20. Where do many feather stars live? _____

Ecology of Echinoderms (page 738)

21. What is the effect of a sudden rise or fall in the number of echinoderms in a marine

habitat? _____

22. Circle the letter of each sentence that is true about the ecology of echinoderms.

a. The crown-of-thorns sea star is a major threat to coral reefs.

b. Sea urchins help control the distribution of algae.

c. Echinoderms feed almost exclusively on coral.

d. Sea stars help control the number of clams and corals.

Vocabulary Review

Labeling Diagrams *Use terms from Chapter 28 to label the diagram below.*

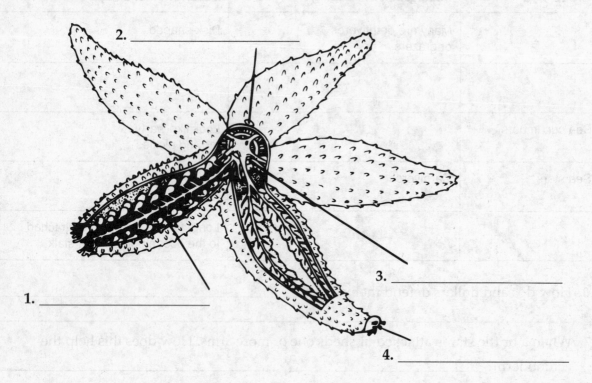

2. _____

3. _____

1. _____

4. _____

Completion *Fill in the blanks with terms from Chapter 28.*

5. A(An) _____ is a tough external covering of the body.

6. A structure that extends from the body wall of an arthropod is called a(an)

_____.

7. The chewing mouthparts of crustaceans are called _____.

8. Chelicerates have _____ pairs of walking legs.

9. Arachnids include mites, ticks, scorpions, and _____.

10. Insects have a body divided into three parts—a head, a(an) _____, and an abdomen.

11. In complete metamorphosis, the stage in which an insect changes from larva to adult is

called a(an) _____.

12. Specific chemical messengers that affect the behavior or development of individuals of

the same insect species are called _____.

13. A(An) _____ is an internal skeleton.

14. Most echinoderms exhibit five-part _____ symmetry.

Chapter 28 Arthropods and Echinoderms   **Section Review 28-1**

Reviewing Key Concepts

Short Answer *On the lines provided, describe the three main features of arthropods.*

1. _____
2. _____
3. _____

Short Answer *On the lines provided, answer the following questions.*

4. How have the number of body segments in arthropods changed during the course of evolution?

_____

_____

5. During the process of evolution, how have the appendages of arthropods changed?

_____

_____

6. Describe the function and process of molting.

_____

_____

_____

Reviewing Key Skills

7. **Inferring** What adaptation in the exoskeletons of terrestrial arthropods prevents water loss? What advantage does this give the arthropod?

_____

_____

8. **Comparing and Contrasting** Compare and contrast book lungs and tracheal tubes.

_____

_____

_____

9. **Comparing and Contrasting** Compare the processes of excretion used by terrestrial and aquatic arthropods.

_____

_____

_____

10. **Applying Concepts** Explain how an arthropod uses its muscles to move its exoskeleton.

_____

_____

Chapter 28 Arthropods and Echinoderms

Reviewing Key Concepts

Completion *On the lines provided, complete the following sentences.*

1. Arthropods are classified based on the number and structure of their

   _____ and appendages.

2. The appendages that are especially important in arthropod

   classification are _____.

Matching *On the lines provided, write the letter of the group of arthropods that best matches each description on the left.*

_____ 3. have two pairs of branched antennae   a. crustaceans

_____ 4. have one pair of antennae   b. uniramians

_____ 5. include crabs, shrimp, and lobsters   c. chelicerates

_____ 6. have mouthparts called chelicerae

_____ 7. include spiders and ticks

_____ 8. have jaws

_____ 9. usually have four pairs of legs

_____ 10. include centipedes, millipedes, and insects

_____ 11. have unbranched appendages

Reviewing Key Skills

12. **Inferring** How does the structure of swimmerets enable a crayfish to move?

   _____

   _____

13. **Applying Concepts** How does a spider use the two modified appendages near its mouth for feeding?

   _____

   _____

14. **Inferring** After capturing its prey, why does a spider wait before eating it?

   _____

   _____

   _____

15. **Classifying** Unlike centipedes, millipedes lack jaws that produce venom. Why would venom-producing glands be useless to millipedes?

   _____

   _____

   _____

Chapter 28 Arthropods and Echinoderms   **Section Review 28-3**

Reviewing Key Concepts

Completion *On the lines provided, complete the following sentences.*

1. The three parts of an insect's body are the _____,

   _____, and _____.

2. Three pairs of legs attach to the _____ of an insect.

3. _____ usually feed in completely different
   ways from adult insects.

4. Ants, bees, and termites are examples of insects that form complex

   arrangements called _____.

Identifying Processes *On the lines provided, identify which of the following type of metamorphosis is shown:* incomplete metamorphosis *or* complete metamorphosis.

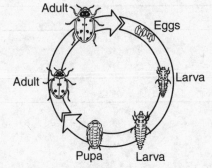

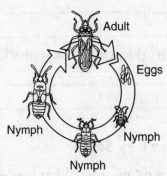

5. _____   6. _____

Reviewing Key Skills

7. **Applying Concepts** How is a moth's mouthpart specialized to its feeding habits?

   _____

   _____

8. **Applying Concepts** Would a pheromone released by a red-ant species
   affect the behavior of a member of a black-ant colony? Explain your answer.

   _____

   _____

9. **Comparing and Contrasting** Describe three ways in which insects attract mates.

   _____

   _____

10. **Applying Concepts** A honeybee has found a food source of great energy value
    close to the hive. How would the bee communicate this information to the rest of
    the bees in the hive?

    _____

    _____

Chapter 28 Arthropods and Echinoderms   Section Review 28-4

Reviewing Key Concepts

Identifying Structures *On the lines provided, list five characteristics of echinoderms.*

1. _____
2. _____
3. _____
4. _____
5. _____

Short Answer *On the lines provided, answer the following questions.*

6. What are three essential body functions carried out by the water vascular system?

_____

_____

7. What are the major classes of echinoderms?

_____

_____

Reviewing Key Skills

8. **Applying Concepts** What has led scientists to believe that echinoderms are more closely related to humans and other vertebrates than to cnidarians?

_____

_____

_____

9. **Applying Concepts** Describe the process that allows a tube foot to hold on to an object.

_____

_____

_____

10. **Comparing and Contrasting** How are the feeding methods used by sea lilies and sea stars similar? How are they different?

_____

_____

_____

Chapter 28 Arthropods and Echinoderms   Chapter Vocabulary Review

Matching *On the lines provided, write the letter of the description that best matches each term on the left.*

_____ **1.** thorax

_____ **2.** chitin

_____ **3.** appendage

_____ **4.** spiracle

_____ **5.** book lung

_____ **6.** Malpighian tubule

_____ **7.** molting

a. shedding of the exoskeleton

b. saclike organ of terrestrial arthropods used to extract waste from the blood

c. made of layered respiratory tissue

d. body section behind the head that houses most of the internal organs

e. a leg or an antenna

f. material in an exoskeleton

g. small opening where air enters and leaves the body of an arthropod

Labeling Diagrams *On the lines provided, label the structures of a crayfish as one of the following:* abdomen, swimmeret, cheliped, mandible, cephalothorax, *and* carapace.

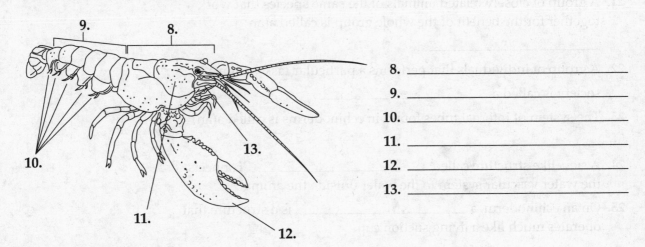

8. _____

9. _____

10. _____

11. _____

12. _____

13. _____

Multiple Choice *On the lines provided, write the letter of the answer that best completes the sentence or answers the question.*

_____ **14.** Horseshoe crabs respire through organs called

    a. tracheal tubes.   **c.** book lungs.

    b. book gills.   **d.** spiracles.

_____ **15.** The mouthpart of a spider that contains a fang is called a

    a. spinneret.   **c.** chelicera.

    b. pedipalp.   **d.** thorax.

_____ **16.** What immature form of an insect looks very much
like an adult?

    a. pupa   c. larva

    b. nymph   d. egg

_____ **17.** Animals that hatch into larvae that look and act
nothing like their parents go through a process called

    a. complete metamorphosis.   c. adolescence.

    b. incomplete metamorphosis.   d. puberty.

_____ **18.** What chemicals do insects use to communicate?

    a. nymphs   c. castes

    b. chelicerae   d. pheromones

Completion *On the lines provided, complete the following sentences.*

19. Most terrestrial arthropods breathe through a network of branching

_____.

20. Spiders have mouthparts called _____ that are
adapted to grab prey.

21. A group of closely related animals of the same species that work
together for the benefit of the whole group is called a(an)

_____.

22. A group of individuals that performs a particular task within a

society is called a _____.

23. The system of internal tubes found in echinoderms is called a(an)

_____.

24. A sievelike structure called a _____ connects
the water vascular system to the water outside the animal.

25. On an echinoderm, a _____ is a structure that
operates much like a living suction cup.

Chapter 28 Arthropods and Echinoderms   Enrichment

Life in Ant Colonies

A colony of ants might contain just a few ants, more than 2 million ants, or any number of ants in between. Most of the ants in a colony are female workers. The colony also includes a few males, who have wings and live only to mate with the queen.

Male ants are produced from unfertilized eggs; the females develop from fertilized eggs. Each ant is born to perform a specific task, such as gathering food, maintaining the colony, or rearing eggs. Female ants are responsible for maintaining the entire colony. Most female ants are nonreproducing, wingless workers. A few are queens, who produce the eggs for the entire colony.

Different ant species create specific types and shapes of colonies and have various methods of obtaining food. Army ants, for example, often migrate to new nesting sites. Along the way, they feed on everything in their path, raiding for food and carrying it to temporary nests. Army ants can build temporary nest sites every day for weeks. Eventually, they might settle in one site for several weeks while the queen lays her eggs and the new ants are reared. Leaf-cutter ants grow fungus for food. They cut and collect leaves and bring them back to the colony. The ants grow a nutritious fungus garden on the moist leaves. The ants excavate chambers in the ground in which the leaves and fungus can be stored and kept moist. Harvester ants eat seeds and live in elaborately excavated colonies. Their nests have entire chambers devoted to the storage of seeds.

Other ants collect "honeydew," a solution that insects such as treehoppers and aphids produce from plant juices and then excrete. Honeydew contains nutrients the ants can use. The ants will try to protect the insects whose honeydew they collect. Some ants even build shelters for honeydew-producing insects.

In some ant species, plant liquids are stored inside special worker ants. The workers are immobilized and suspended from the ceilings of the nests, providing living food storage for other ants.

Evaluation *On the lines provided, answer the following questions.*

1. What are some differences between male and female ants?

_____

_____

_____

_____

2. How do the specialized colonies of leaf-cutter ants and harvester ants reflect their feeding habits?

_____

_____

_____

_____

Chapter 28 Arthropods and Echinoderms   Graphic Organizer

Compare/Contrast Table

Using information from the chapter, complete the compare/contrast table below to compare different groups of arthropods. If there is not enough room in the table to write your answers, write them on a separate sheet of paper.

Group	Chelicerates	1.	2.
Examples	3.	Crayfish, lobsters, shrimp	Bees, flies, grasshoppers, millipedes, centipedes
Number of Body Sections	4.	Two: cephalothorax and abdomen; or three: head, thorax, and abdomen	Varies widely
Mouthparts	5.	6.	7.
Number of Antennae	None	8.	9.
Number of Legs	10.	Five or more pairs	Varies widely

Chapter 28 Arthropods and Echinoderms   **Chapter Test A**

Multiple Choice

Write the letter that best answers the question or completes the statement on the line provided.

_____ 1. The appendages of arthropods are
     a. found only on the head.
     b. hard and immovable.
     c. jointed and extend from the body wall.
     d. divided into six branches.

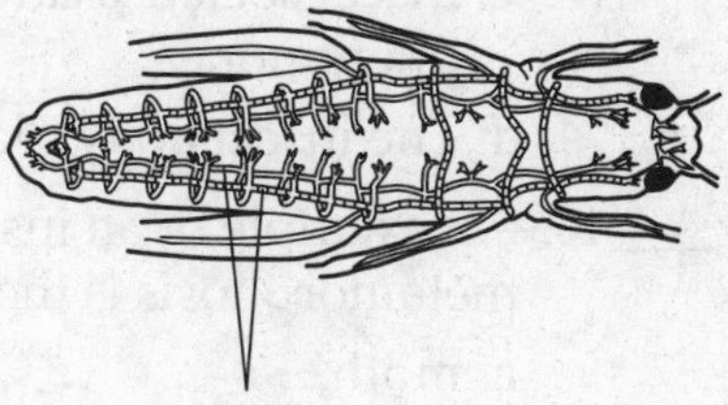

X

Figure 1

_____ 2. The structures labeled X in Figure 1 are filled with
     a. water.   c. air.
     b. blood.   d. nitrogenous wastes.

_____ 3. All of the following are true about arthropods EXCEPT that
     a. they have a closed circulatory system.
     b. they have an exoskeleton made of chitin.
     c. they include herbivores, carnivores, and omnivores.
     d. they move using muscles controlled by the nervous system.

_____ 4. An arthropod is vulnerable to predators during the molting period because
     a. it must come out of hiding to molt.
     b. its new exoskeleton is soft.
     c. molting cannot occur without the assistance of predators.
     d. predators are more numerous during this period.

_____ 5. The function of mandibles is to
     a. bite and grind food.
     b. sense the environment.
     c. propel an arthropod when it swims.
     d. support an arthropod when it walks.

_____ 6. An example of a chelicerate is a
     a. lobster.   c. crayfish.
     b. centipede.   d. spider.

_____ 7. Spiders feed by
     a. swallowing their prey whole.
     b. biting off and swallowing pieces of their prey.
     c. sucking up prey tissues that have been liquefied by enzymes.
     d. sipping nectar through a tubelike mouthpart.

_____ 8. An insect can detect minute movements in its environment by using its compound eyes and its
     a. Malpighian tubules.   c. chelicerae.
     b. tracheal tubes.   d. sensory hairs.

____ 9. Which of the following explains why flying has been beneficial to insects?

    a. Nymphs can escape most predators.

    b. Insects can disperse long distances and colonize a variety of habitats.

    c. Insect societies can communicate without using pheromones.

    d. The insect body plan can function with only two sections.

____ 10. An example of an insect that undergoes incomplete metamorphosis is the

    a. moth.   c. beetle.

    b. bee.   d. chinch bug.

____ 11. Which of the following is NOT true about insect societies?

    a. All species use the same "language" of visual and chemical signals.

    b. Individuals may be specialized to perform particular roles.

    c. Every individual in a society works for the benefit of the whole group.

    d. Each caste has a body form specialized for its role.

____ 12. In most species of echinoderms, respiration occurs mainly in the

    a. tube feet.   c. ring canal.

    b. madreporite.   d. radial canals.

____ 13. The skeleton of an echinoderm is an

    a. exoskeleton made of calcium carbonate.

    b. exoskeleton made of chitin.

    c. endoskeleton made of calcium carbonate.

    d. endoskeleton made of chitin.

____ 14. The water vascular system of echinoderms is involved with each of the following body functions EXCEPT

    a. respiration.   c. movement.

    b. circulation.   d. reproduction.

____ 15. In the Great Barrier Reef of Australia, extensive areas of coral have been destroyed by the crown of thorns, which is a type of

    a. sea cucumber.   c. sea star.

    b. sea urchin.   d. sea lily.

Completion

Complete each statement on the line provided.

16. In arthropods, ganglia are located along a ventral _____ .

17. If an arthropod has two pairs of antennae and two or three body sections, it is classified as a _____ .

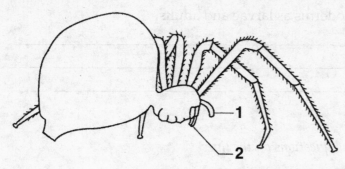

Figure 2

18. In the spider in Figure 2, the appendages labeled 1 are called _____ .

19. In the spider in Figure 2, the appendages labeled 2, which contain mouthparts, are called _____ .

20. In an echinoderm, oxygen is carried throughout the body by the _____ system.

Short Answer

In complete sentences, write the answers to the questions on the lines provided.

21. Name the three sections of an insect's body and the two sections of a chelicerate's body.

_____

_____

22. Identify the respiratory organs used by spiders.

_____

_____

23. Name two ways in which insects are beneficial to humans.

_____

_____

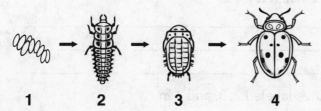

Figure 3

24. Figure 3 shows the development of a ladybug. Identify the stages labeled 1 through 4.

_____

_____

25. Contrast the body symmetry of echinoderms as larvae and adults.

_____

_____

_____

Using Science Skills

Use the diagram below to answer the following questions on the lines provided.

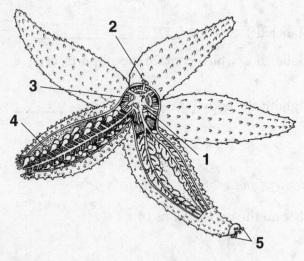

Figure 4

26. Applying Concepts What type of body symmetry is shown by the sea star in Figure 4? How do you know?

_____

_____

_____

_____

27. Applying Concepts What is the structure labeled 1 in Figure 4? Explain how the sea star uses this structure when it feeds.

_____

_____

_____

28. Interpreting Graphics Identify the structures labeled 2, 3, and 4 in Figure 4.

_____

_____

_____

29. **Applying Concepts** What are the structures labeled 5 in Figure 4? Describe the role of these structures in movement.

_____

_____

_____

_____

_____

_____

30. **Applying Concepts** How do tube feet help a sea star obtain food.

_____

_____

_____

_____

_____

_____

Essay

Write the answer to each question in the space provided.

31. Describe the events that take place when an arthropod molts.

32. Describe the external structural differences between spiders and insects.

33. Compare and contrast centipedes and millipedes.

34. Explain how a worker honeybee communicates the location of food that is more than 50 meters from the hive.

35. Describe reproduction and development in sea stars.

Multiple Choice

Write the letter that best answers the question or completes the statement on the line provided.

_____ **1.** Most terrestrial arthropods breathe through a network of air-filled tubes called
   a. tracheal tubes.
   b. Malpighian tubules.
   c. book gills.

_____ **2.** Which of the following habitats do arthropods occupy?
   a. the sea
   b. the land
   c. both a and b

_____ **3.** What does molting enable arthropods to do?
   a. to breathe
   b. to reproduce
   c. to grow

_____ **4.** Arthropods are classified based on the number and structure of their
   a. eyes and wings.
   b. body segments and appendages.
   c. muscles and bones.

_____ **5.** Insects are classified as
   a. crustaceans.
   b. arachnids.
   c. uniramians.

_____ **6.** How many pairs of legs are there on most body segments of a centipede?
   a. one
   b. two
   c. five

_____ **7.** The compound eyes of insects
   a. are made of many lenses.
   b. are located on the thorax.
   c. are not very good at detecting movement.

_____ **8.** The body of an insect is divided into a
   a. head and a thorax.
   b. head and a cephalothorax.
   c. head, a thorax, and an abdomen.

____ **9.** Which of the following is NOT a stage of complete metamorphosis?
　　a. nymph
　　b. egg
　　c. larva

____**10.** In most ant societies, egg laying is performed by
　　a. the workers.
　　b. one queen.
　　c. hundreds of queens.

____**11.** In echinoderms, body parts usually occur in multiples of
　　a. two.
　　b. five.
　　c. three.

____**12.** In an echinoderm, the structure that operates like a living suction cup is the
　　a. madreporite.
　　b. tube foot.
　　c. stomach.

____**13.** Which structure is part of an echinoderm's water vascular system?
　　a. skin gill
　　b. stomach
　　c. madreporite

____**14.** The echinoderms that look like warty, moving pickles are
　　a. sea urchins.
　　b. sea cucumbers.
　　c. sea stars.

____**15.** Two echinoderms that are in the same class are
　　a. sea urchins and sand dollars.
　　b. sea stars and sea cucumbers.
　　c. sea cucumbers and sea urchins.

Completion

Complete each statement on the line provided.

16. A typical primitive arthropod had many identical _____, each with a pair of appendages.

17. An arthropod's exoskeleton is made of_____ .

18. Chelicerae contain mouth parts called _____ that stab and paralyze prey.

19. Insects have _____ pairs of legs.

20. Within a society, particular tasks or roles are performed by groups of individuals called _____ .

Short Answer

In complete sentences, write the answers to the questions on the lines provided.

21. List three features that are present in the body plan of arthropods.

_____

_____

22. Suppose you observed an arthropod whose body was divided into a cephalothorax and an abdomen. Which of the three major groups of arthropods could this specimen belong to?

_____

_____

23. How are mites and ticks harmful to humans?

_____

_____

_____

_____

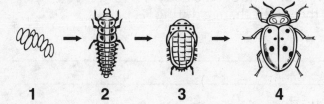

1   2   3   4

Figure 1

24. What type of metamorphosis is shown in Figure 1?

_____

_____

_____

_____

25. What will happen if a sea star is pulled into pieces?

_____

_____

_____

_____

Using Science Skills

Use the chart below to answer the following questions on the lines provided.

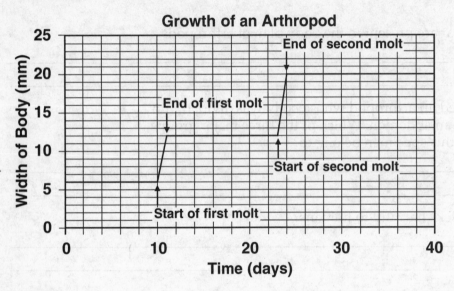

Figure 2

26. **Calculating** Figure 2 shows how the width of an arthropod's body changed over time. By what amounts did the width change during the first and second molts?

_____

_____

27. **Inferring** Explain why the width of the arthropod's body changed during each molt in Figure 2.

_____

_____

28. **Using Tables and Graphs** In Figure 2 what was the width of the arthropod's body between the end of the first molt and the start of the second molt?

_____

29. **Inferring** Explain why the width of the arthropod's body did not change between the end of the first molt and the start of the second molt in Figure 2.

_____

_____

_____

30. **Using Tables and Graphs** In Figure 2, how long did it take for the width of the arthropod's body to increase from 6 mm to 20 mm?

_____

_____

LESSON PLAN 29–1 (pages 745–750)

Invertebrate Evolution

Time
2 periods
1 block

Section Objectives

Local Standards

- **29.1.1 Explain** what the Cambrian Explosion was.
- **29.1.2 Describe** the major trends in invertebrate evolution.

Vocabulary radial symmetry • bilateral symmetry • cephalization • coelom

1 FOCUS

Reading Strategy
Before reading, students each write a paragraph explaining what they already know about the history of life.

Targeted Resources
❏ Transparencies: **440** Section 29–1 Interest Grabber
❏ Transparencies: **441** Section 29–1 Outline
❏ Transparencies: **442** Compare/Contrast Table

2 INSTRUCT

Make Connections: Earth Science
Place the Cambrian organisms of the Burgess Shale in context by displaying and reviewing a geologic time scale. **L2**

Build Science Skills: Inferring
Construct a classroom display of various invertebrates, and challenge students to infer how closely the invertebrates are related to one another. **L2**

Use Visuals: Figure 29–4
Use Figure 29–4 to reinforce an understanding of relationships among groups of animals. **L1 L2**

Use Visuals: Figure 29–5
Use Figure 29–5 to review the major characteristics of the main groups of invertebrates. **L2 L3**

Problem Solving
Students create an imaginary invertebrate that lives in a specific habitat that students imagine and describe. **L2 L3**

Targeted Resources
❏ Reading and Study Workbook: Section 29–1
❏ Adapted Reading and Study Workbook: Section 29–1
❏ Transparencies: **443** Figure 29–4 Invertebrate Cladogram
❏ Teaching Resources: Section Summaries 29–1, Worksheets 29–1, Enrichment

3 ASSESS

Evaluate Understanding
Call on students to explain the major trends of invertebrate evolution.

Reteach
Have students describe invertebrate evolution, using Figure 29–4 as a reference.

Targeted Resources
Teaching Resources: Section Review 29–1
❏ *i Text* Section 29–1

LESSON PLAN 29–2 (pages 751–758)

Form and Function in Invertebrates

Time
3 periods
1 1/2 block

Section Objective
Local Standards

■ **29.2.1 Describe** how the different invertebrate phyla
carry out their essential life functions.

Vocabulary intracellular digestion • extracellular digestion
• open circulatory system • closed circulatory system
• hydrostatic skeleton • exoskeleton • endoskeleton
• external fertilization • internal fertilization

1 FOCUS

Vocabulary Preview
Have students locate each Vocabulary word in
the section and read its definition.

Targeted Resources
❏ Transparencies: **444** Section 29–2 Interest
Grabber, **445** Section 29–2 Outline

2 INSTRUCT

Use Visuals: Figure 29–8
Use Figure 29–8 to reinforce an understanding
of intracellular and extracellular digestion. **L2**

Build Science Skills: Using Analogies
Compare diffusion of gas through skin to
absorption of water by paper towels. **L1 L2**

Quick Lab
Students investigate gas exchange in clams and
crayfishes. **L2 L3**

**Build Science Skills: Comparing and
Contrasting**
Groups of students research and create displays
that focus on the essential functions of groups
of invertebrates. **L1 L2**

Demonstration
Have students observe how live planarians in a
petri dish avoid light. **L1 L2**

Targeted Resources
❏ Reading and Study Workbook: Section 29–2

❏ Adapted Reading and Study Workbook:
Section 29–2

❏ Teaching Resources: Section Summaries
29–2, Worksheets 29–2

❏ Transparencies: **446** Types of Invertebrate
Skeletons, **447** Figure 29–8 Invertebrate
Digestive Systems, **448** Figure 29–9
Invertebrate Respiratory Systems, **449** Figure
29–10 Invertebrate Circulatory Systems,
450 Figure 29–11 Invertebrate Excretory
Systems, **451** Figure 29–12 Invertebrate
Nervous Systems

❏ Lab Worksheets: Chapter 29 Design an
Experiment

❏ Lab Manual A: Chapter 29 Lab

❏ Lab Manual B: Chapter 29 Lab

❏ **NSTA** *sci*$_{LINKS}$ Invertebrates

3 ASSESS

Evaluate Understanding
Ask students to provide support for each of the
section's boldface sentences.

Reteach
Students write a paragraph comparing two
animals from different phyla in terms of their
essential functions.

Targeted Resources
❏ Teaching Resources: Section Review 29–2,
Chapter Vocabulary Review, Graphic
Organizer, Chapter 29 Tests: Levels A and B

❏ Lab Assessment: Laboratory Assessment 8

❏ **⟨ⓘText⟩** Section 29–2, Chapter 29
Assessment

❏ **PHSchool.com** Online Chapter 29 Test

Chapter 29   Comparing Invertebrates

Summary

29–1 Invertebrate Evolution

Paleontologists have identified microscopic fossils from 570 to 610 million years ago. They identified trace fossils from the same time period. Trace fossils are tracks and burrows made by soft-bodied animals.

Fossils of some primitive animals were discovered in the Ediacara Hills of Australia. The Ediacaran animals lived 543 to 575 million years ago. They were flat and plate-shaped. They lived on shallow sea bottoms and had soft, segmented bodies and bilateral symmetry. The animals appear to have lacked cell specialization or a front and a back end.

The Cambrian Period began 544 million years ago. It is marked by many kinds of fossils. The Burgess Shale of Canada is one of the best-known sites of Cambrian fossils. These animals evolved complex body plans. Because of its great growth in animal diversity, events of the early Cambrian Period are called the Cambrian Explosion. The Burgess Shale animals typically had body symmetry, segmentation, some type of skeleton, a front and a back end, and appendages having many functions.

The appearance of each animal phylum in the fossil record shows the evolution of a successful and unique body plan. Modern sponges and cnidarians have little internal specialization. As larger and more complex animals evolved, specialized cells formed tissues, organs, and organ systems.

All invertebrates except sponges have some type of body symmetry.
- Cnidarians and echinoderms have radial symmetry. **Radial symmetry** is a body plan in which the body parts repeat around the center of the body.
- Worms, mollusks, and arthropods have bilateral symmetry. **Bilateral symmetry** is a body plan in which only a single, imaginary line can divide the body into two equal halves.

A trend toward cephalization occurred with the evolution of bilateral symmetry. **Cephalization** is the concentration of sense organs and nerve cells in the front of the body. **Cephalization lets animals respond to the environment in more sophisticated ways.**

Most complex animals are coelomates. They have a true coelom. A coelom is a body cavity lined with tissue derived from mesoderm.

- Flatworms are *acoelomates*—they have no coelom.
- Roundworms are *pseudocoelomates*. Their coelom is only partially lined with mesoderm.
- Mollusks, annelids, arthropods, and echinoderms all have a true coelom.

The zygote of most invertebrates divides to form a blastula. An opening, called the blastopore, then forms in this blastula.

- In protostomes, the blastopore develops into a mouth. Worms, arthropods, and mollusks are protostomes.
- In deuterostomes, the blastopore develops into an anus. Echinoderms (and chordates) are deuterostomes.

29–2 Form and Function in Invertebrates

Biologists learn a great deal about the nature of life by comparing the body systems of the various living invertebrates. All animals perform the same essential tasks: feeding and digestion, respiration, circulation, excretion, response, movement and support, and reproduction.

Feeding **The simplest animals—sponges—break down food inside their cells. Mollusks, annelids, arthropods, and echinoderms use extracellular digestion.** Food is broken down outside the cells of a digestive tract. Food enters the body through the mouth, and wastes leave through the anus.

Respiration **All respiratory systems share two features.**
(1) Respiratory organs have a large surface area that is in contact with air or water.
(2) Respiratory surfaces must be moist for diffusion to occur.

Aquatic mollusks, arthropods, and many annelids exchange gases through gills. In land animals, surfaces are covered with water or mucus. Such covering prevents water loss from the body. It also moistens air moving through the respiratory system.

Circulation All cells need a constant supply of oxygen and nutrients. They also must remove wastes. The smallest and thinnest animals exchange materials with the environment by diffusion. **More complex animals use a system of pumps and tubes for transport.** There are two types of circulatory systems.

- In an open circulatory system, blood is only partly contained within blood vessels. The blood moves through the vessels into a system of sinuses, where the blood comes into direct contact with the tissues.
- In a closed circulatory system, blood moves throughout the body in vessels. The blood moves under force from a heart or heartlike organ.

Excretion Multicellular animals must control the amount of water in their tissues. They also must get rid of ammonia, a toxic nitrogen waste formed during metabolism. **Most animals have an excretory system to rid the body of metabolic wastes. The excretory system also controls the amount of water in the tissues.** Aquatic organisms get rid of ammonia through diffusion. Many land animals convert ammonia into urea. This compound is then eliminated from the body in urine.

Response The more complex an animal's nervous system is, the more developed its sense organs are. **Invertebrates show three trends in the evolution of the nervous system: centralization, cephalization, and specialization.** Simple animals have nerve cells that are spread through the body, while more complex animals have centralized nerve cells. More complex animals also have more highly specialized sense organs.

Support and Movement **Invertebrates have one of three main kinds of skeletal systems.**

- Annelids and certain cnidarians have a **hydrostatic skeleton.** In this system, muscles surround a fluid-filled body cavity that supports the muscles. The muscles contract and push against the water.
- Arthropods have an **exoskeleton,** or external skeleton.
- Echinoderms have an **endoskeleton,** a structural support located inside the body.

Reproduction **Some invertebrates may reproduce asexually. However, most reproduce sexually at some part of their life cycle.** Asexual reproduction allows animals to reproduce rapidly. Sexual reproduction maintains genetic diversity in a population by creating individuals with new combinations of genes. Most animals have separate sexes that produce eggs or sperm.

- In **external fertilization,** eggs are fertilized outside the female's body.
- In **internal fertilization,** eggs are fertilized inside the female's body.

Major Adaptations in Animal Evolution

The cladogram shows one theory of the evolution of animals.
Each circle represents the evolution of an important adaptation in
animal development.

Follow the prompts to interpret the cladogram.
- Color the organism(s) that have a pseudocoelom brown.
- Color the organism(s) that have radial symmetry blue.
- Color the organism(s) that are deuterostomes red.
- Circle the organism(s) that have a true coelom.

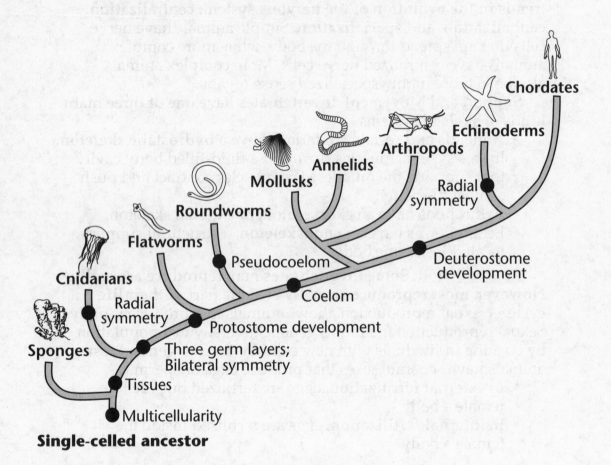

Use the cladogram to answer the question. Circle the correct answer.

1. Which evolved earlier?

coelom   bilateral symmetry

Comparing Invertebrates

Invertebrates have a variety of body plans. During development, two or three germ layers may develop. Some invertebrates do not have any germ layers. They can have no body symmetry, radial symmetry, or bilateral symmetry. Some show cephalization, and others do not.

Complete the table. Some information has been filled in for you.

Organism	Germ Layers During Development	Body Symmetry	Cephalization
Sponges	none	none	no
Cnidarians	two		
Flatworms			yes
Roundworms		bilateral	
Annelids			yes
Mollusks	three		
Arthropods	three		
Adult Echinoderms		radial	

Coelom Evolution

The embryos of most animals develop three layers of cells, called germ layers: the ectoderm, endoderm, and mesoderm. These layers develop into different structures in different animals. Some animals develop a coelom, or fluid-filled cavity lined with mesoderm.

Color the ectoderm in each diagram red. Color the mesoderm blue. Color the endoderm yellow.

Acoelomate

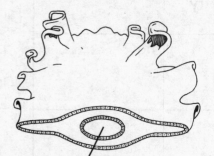

Digestive cavity

Pseudocoelomate

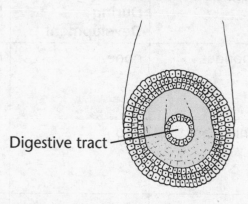

Digestive tract

Coelomate

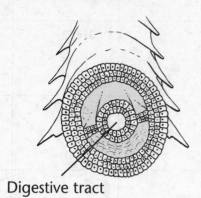

Digestive tract

Use the diagrams to answer the questions.

1. Which type of organism does not have a digestive tract?

_____

2. Which term describes a flatworm? Circle the correct answer.

acoelomate   pseudocoelomate   coelomate

Invertebrate Digestive Systems

Most invertebrates have a mouth through which they consume food and an anus through which wastes are removed. In some animals, the same structure serves as both mouth and anus. These structures are part of the digestive system.

Color the digestive system in each organism blue. Then label the mouth *and* anus *on each diagram.*

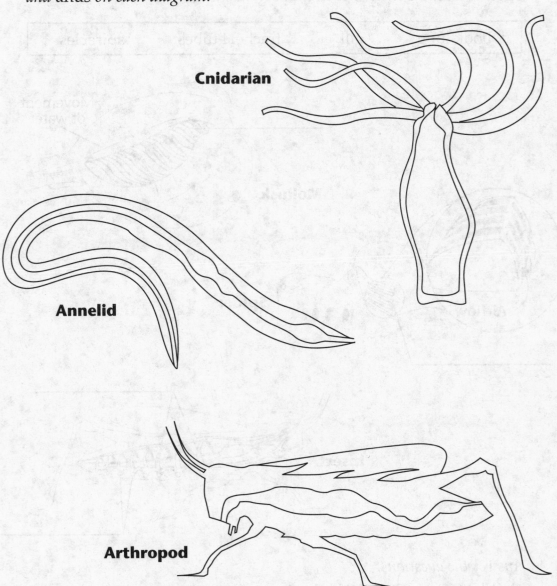

Cnidarian

Annelid

Arthropod

Use the diagrams to answer the question.

1. Which organism has a digestive system with only one opening?

_____

Invertebrate Respiratory Systems

Invertebrates have a variety of respiratory systems. Aquatic invertebrates may have gills to obtain oxygen from water. Land invertebrates may use structures including book lungs and tracheal tubes to obtain oxygen from the air.

Color the respiratory system in each organism red. Then use the words below to label the structures in each organism.

book lung	gill	tracheal tubes	spiracles

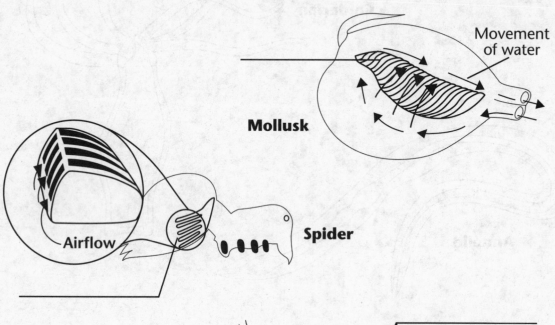

Mollusk

Movement of water

Airflow

Spider

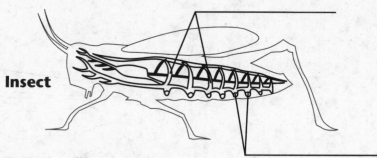

Insect

Answer the questions.

1. What can you conclude about a mollusk that uses gills for respiration?

_____

2. What are spiracles?

_____

_____

Invertebrate Circulatory Systems

In an open circulatory system, the hearts or heartlike organs pump blood into cavities called sinuses. The blood contacts tissues directly and eventually returns to the heart. In a closed circulatory system, the hearts or heartlike organs pump blood through vessels.

Color the circulatory system in each organism red. Label the hearts and blood vessels in the grasshopper and the heartlike structures and blood vessels in the earthworm.

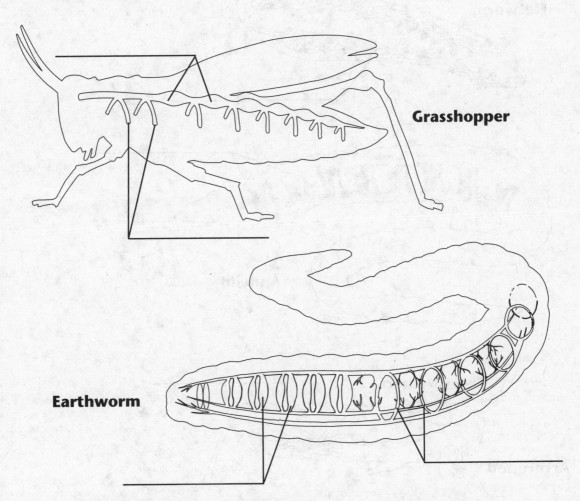

Grasshopper

Earthworm

Use the diagrams to answer the questions. Circle the correct answer.

1. What kind of circulatory system does the grasshopper have?

    closed   open

2. What kind of circulatory system does the earthworm have?

    closed   open

Invertebrate Excretory Systems

The excretory system in animals removes wastes from the body. Invertebrates have evolved different structures, such as flame cells, Malpighian tubules, and nephridia, to accomplish this task.

Color the excretory structures in each organism blue. Then label the flame cells, Malpighian tubules, *and* nephridia.

Flatworm

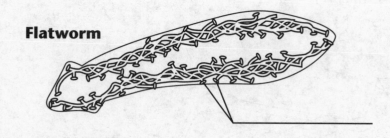

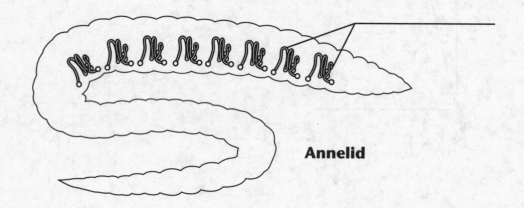

Annelid

Digestive tract

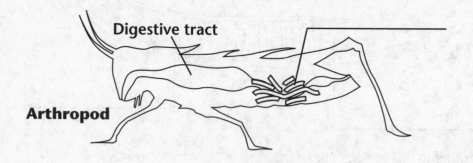

Arthropod

Use the diagrams to answer the questions.

1. Which organism uses nephridia to remove wastes?

_____

2. Explain how flame cells are used.

_____

Invertebrate Nervous Systems

The nervous system controls an animal's response to its environment. Many animals have a brain or groups of nerve cells called *ganglia* that control the nervous system.

Label the nervous system structures in the following invertebrates. Choose from the following labels: nerve cells, brain, *and* ganglia. *Some words may be used more than once.*

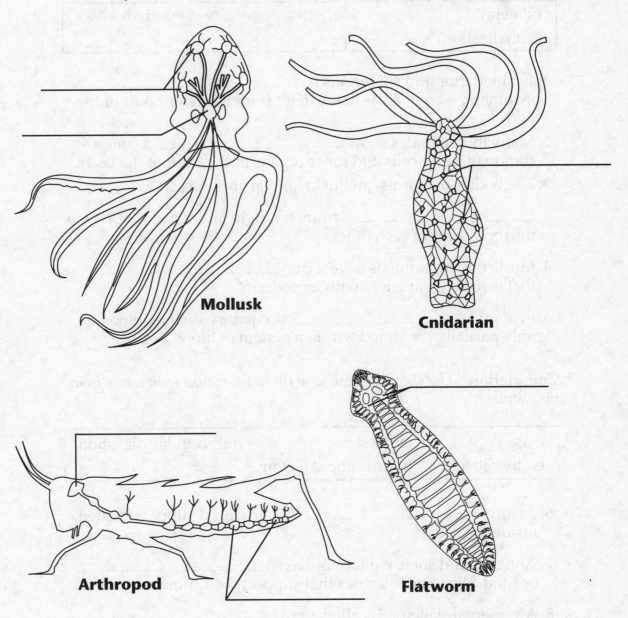

Mollusk

Cnidarian

Arthropod

Flatworm

Use the diagrams to answer the question.

1. Which organism shows cephalization? Circle the correct answer.

     mollusk   cnidarian

Chapter 29 Comparing Invertebrates

Vocabulary Review

Completion *Use the words below to fill in the blanks with terms from the chapter.*

bilateral	coelom	radial
cephalization	open	

1. Echinoderms and cnidarians have _____ symmetry—body parts that extend from the center part of the body.

2. Many invertebrates show _____, a concentration of nerve cells and sense organs in the front of the body.

3. The bodies of worms, mollusks, and arthropods show

   _____ symmetry, right and left sides that are mirror images of each other.

4. Most complex animals have a true _____ that is lined completely with mesoderm.

5. In a(an) _____ circulatory system, blood is only partially contained within a system of blood vessels.

Completion *Use the words below to fill in the blanks with terms from the chapter.*

closed	exoskeleton	intracellular digestion
endoskeleton	hydrostatic skeletons	

6. A(An) _____ is a structural support located inside the body.

7. Annelids and some cnidarians have _____, or fluid-filled body cavities that support their muscles.

8. An external skeleton is called a(an) _____.

9. In a(an) _____ circulatory system, a heart or heartlike organ pumps blood through a system of enclosed blood vessels.

10. The simplest animals digest their food inside cells in a process

    known as _____.

Summary

29–1 Invertebrate Evolution

Paleontologists have identified microscopic fossils from between 610 and 570 million years ago. From the same time period, they have identified trace fossils, which are tracks and burrows made by soft-bodied animals. The fossils of some of the earliest and most primitive animals known were discovered in the Ediacara Hills of Australia. The Ediacaran animals, which lived between 575 and 543 million years ago, were flat and plate-shaped. They lived on the bottom of shallow seas and were made of soft tissues. They were segmented and had bilateral symmetry. However, the fossils show little evidence of cell specialization or a front and back end.

The Cambrian Period, which began 544 million years ago, is marked by the abundance of different fossils. One of the best-known sites of Cambrian fossils is the Burgess Shale of Canada. In just a few million years, animals had evolved complex body plans. Because of the extraordinary growth in animal diversity, events of the early Cambrian Period are called the Cambrian Explosion. The anatomies of Burgess Shale animals typically had body symmetry, segmentation, some type of skeleton, a front and a back end, and appendages adapted for many functions.

The appearance of each animal phylum in the fossil record represents the evolution of a successful and unique body plan. Modern sponges and cnidarians have little internal specialization. As larger and more complex animals have evolved, specialized cells join together to form tissues, organs, and organ systems.

All invertebrates except sponges exhibit some type of symmetry. Cnidarians and echinoderms exhibit radial symmetry—body parts extend from the center of the body.

Worms, mollusks, and arthropods exhibit bilateral symmetry—they have mirror-image right and left sides. The evolution of bilateral symmetry was accompanied by the trend toward cephalization, which is the concentration of sense organs and nerve cells in the front of the body. Invertebrates with cephalization can respond to the environment in more sophisticated ways than can simpler invertebrates.

Most complex animals are coelomates, with a true coelom that is lined with tissue derived from mesoderm. A coelom is a body cavity. Flatworms are acoelomates—they don't have a coelom. Roundworms are pseudocoelomates—their coelom is only partially lined with mesoderm. Annelids, mollusks, arthropods, and echinoderms have true coeloms.

In most invertebrates, the zygote divides to form a blastula. In protostomes, the blastopore develops into a mouth. In deuterostomes, the blastopore develops into an anus. Worms, arthropods, and mollusks are protostomes. Echinoderms (and chordates) are deuterostomes.

29–2 Form and Function in Invertebrates

In many ways, each animal phylum represents an "experiment" in the adaptation of body structures to carry out the essential functions of life. Biologists can learn a great deal about the nature of life by comparing body systems among the various living invertebrates.

The simplest animals—sponges—break down food primarily through intracellular digestion, which is the process of digesting food inside cells. More complex animals—mollusks, annelids, arthropods, and echinoderms—use extracellular digestion, which is the process of breaking down food outside the cells in a digestive cavity or tract. Complex animals digest food in a tube called the digestive tract. Food enters the body through the mouth and leaves the body through the anus.

All respiratory systems share two basic features: (1) Respiratory organs have large surface areas that are in contact with the air or water. (2) For diffusion to occur, the respiratory surfaces must be moist. Aquatic animals naturally have moist respiratory surfaces. Aquatic mollusks, arthropods, and many annelids exchange gases through gills. In terrestrial animals, surfaces are covered with water or mucus. Such covering prevents water loss from the body and also moistens air as it travels through the body to the respiratory surface.

All cells require a constant supply of oxygen and nutrients. Also, cells must remove wastes. The smallest and thinnest animals accomplish these tasks by diffusion between their bodies and the environment. Most complex animals move blood through their bodies using one or more hearts. Some animals use an open circulatory system, in which blood is only partially contained within blood vessels. The blood moves through vessels into a system of sinuses, where the blood directly contacts tissues. Other animals have a closed circulatory system. In a closed circulatory system, a heart or heartlike organ forces blood through vessels that extend throughout the body.

Multicellular animals must control the amount of water in their tissues. But they also have to get rid of ammonia, a poisonous nitrogen-containing waste produced as a result of metabolism. Most animals have an excretory system that rids the body of metabolic wastes while controlling the amount of water in the tissues. Many land animals convert ammonia into a compound called urea, which is eliminated from the body through urine.

Invertebrates show three trends in the evolution of the nervous system: centralization, cephalization, and specialization. The more complex an animal's nervous system is, the more developed its sense organs are.

Invertebrates have one of three main kinds of skeletal systems: hydrostatic skeletons, exoskeletons, or endoskeletons. Annelids and certain cnidarians have a hydrostatic skeleton, in which muscles surround a fluid-filled body cavity that supports the muscles. Arthropods have an exoskeleton, which is an external skeleton. Echinoderms have an endoskeleton, which is structural support located inside the body.

Most invertebrates reproduce sexually during at least part of their life cycle. Depending on environmental conditions, however, many invertebrates may also reproduce asexually. In external fertilization, eggs are fertilized outside the female's body. In internal fertilization, eggs are fertilized inside the female's body.

Section 29–1 Invertebrate Evolution
(pages 745–750)

🔑 **Key Concept**
- What are the major trends in invertebrate evolution?

Introduction (page 745)

1. What are three places where fossils have been found that shed light on the origins of invertebrates?

    a. _____

    b. _____

    c. _____

Origin of the Invertebrates (pages 745–747)

2. What are trace fossils? _____

    _____

    _____

    _____

3. Circle the letter of how old the fossils of the Ediacaran fauna are.

    a. 700–600 years old

    b. 6500–7500 years old

    c. 60–75 million years old

    d. 610–570 million years old

4. Is the following sentence true or false? Most fossils of Ediacaran fauna show little evidence of cell specialization. _____

5. What is the best known site of Cambrian fossils? _____

    _____

    _____

6. Circle the letter of each sentence that is true about animals of the Burgess Shale.

    a. They were ancestors of most modern animal phyla.

    b. They had features that are characteristic of most invertebrates living today.

    c. They had specialized cells, tissues, and organs.

    d. They were far less diverse than animals that lived earlier.

7. What features of the Burgess Shale animals made them so successful? _____

    _____

    _____

    _____

Invertebrate Phylogeny (page 747)

8. To which group of invertebrates are chordates most closely related?

_____

9. Number the features below according to the sequence in which they evolved. Number the feature that evolved first *1*.

_____ **a.** Deuterostome development

_____ **b.** Tissues

_____ **c.** Coelom

_____ **d.** Protostome development

Evolutionary Trends (pages 748–750)

10. What does the appearance of each phylum in the fossil record represent in terms of evolution? _____

_____

11. As larger and more complex animals evolved, in what ways did specialized cells join together? _____

_____

_____

12. Circle the letter of each animal group that has organ systems.

a. flatworms

b. cnidarians

c. mollusks

d. arthropods

13. What are the two kinds of symmetry that invertebrates exhibit? _____

_____

14. What is cephalization? _____

_____

_____

15. What body plan and lifestyle characterize invertebrates that have evolved cephalization? _____

_____

_____

16. What are the three germ layers that most invertebrates develop from?

a. _____

b. _____

c. _____

17. What is a coelom? _____

18. Label each of the cross sections of the acoelomate, pseudocoelomate, and coelomate.

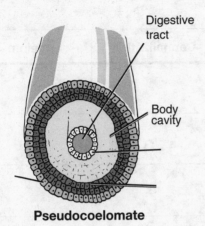

Digestive tract

Body cavity

Pseudocoelomate

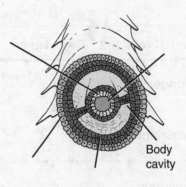

Body cavity

Coelomate

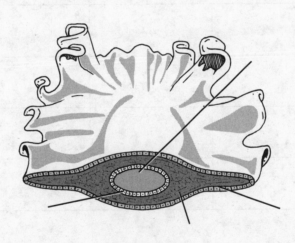

Acoelomate

19. What does segmentation allow an animal to do with a minimum of new genetic material?

_____

20. Most complex animal phyla have a true coelom that is lined completely with

_____.

21. In most invertebrates, the zygote divides repeatedly to form a(an)

_____.

22. What is the difference in early development between a protostome and a

deuterostome? _____

_____

_____

23. Which groups of invertebrates are protostomes? _____

_____

24. Complete the table that shows the general characteristics of the main groups of invertebrates.

Invertebrate	Germ Layer	Body Symmetry	Cephalization	Coelom
Sponges				
Cnidarians				
Flatworms				
Roundworms				
Annelids				
Mollusks				
Arthropods				
Echinoderms				

Reading Skill Practice

A good way to show similarities and differences between items is with a Venn diagram, which consists of two or more circles that overlap. Create Venn diagrams that compare these groups of invertebrates: (1) cnidarians and roundworms, (2) annelids and mollusks, and (3) arthropods and echinoderms. Use the table above for the information to be contained in your diagrams. For more information about Venn diagrams, see Organizing Information in Appendix A of your textbook.

Section 29–2 Form and Function in Invertebrates (pages 751–758)

🔑 Key Concept
• How do different invertebrate phyla carry out life functions?

Introduction (page 751)

1. What are seven essential tasks all animals perform to survive? _____
_____
_____

2. Why aren't more complicated systems in living animals necessarily better than simpler systems in other living animals? _____
_____
_____

Feeding and Digestion (pages 751–752)

3. How is the digestion of food different in simple animals compared to that in more complex animals? _____
_____
_____

4. Complete the table about types of digestion.

TYPES OF DIGESTION

Type	Definition
	Digestion of food inside cells
Extracellular digestion	

5. More-complex animals digest food in a tube called a(an) _____.

Respiration (pages 752–753)

6. Why do respiratory organs have large surface areas? _____
_____
_____

7. Why are respiratory surfaces kept moist? _____
_____

8. What are gills? _____
_____

9. What are book lungs made of? _____
_____

Circulation (page 754)

10. How do the smallest and thinnest animals meet the requirement of supplying oxygen and nutrients to cells and removing metabolic wastes? _____

_____

_____

11. Complex animals move fluid through their bodies using one or more

_____.

12. Label each of the organisms below according to which has a closed circulatory system and which has an open circulatory system.

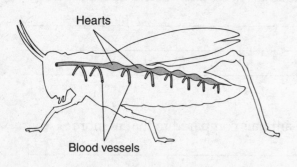

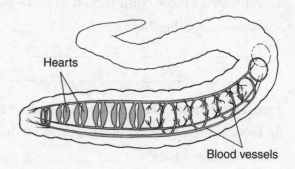

_____   _____

13. Closed circulatory systems are characteristic of what kinds of animals? _____

_____

_____

Excretion (pages 754–755)

14. What does the excretory system of most animals do? _____

_____

_____

15. How do aquatic invertebrates rid their bodies of ammonia? _____

_____

_____

16. Circle the letter of each way that terrestrial invertebrates eliminate nitrogenous wastes from their bodies.

   a. Ammonia diffuses from body tissues into the surrounding water.

   b. They convert ammonia into urea.

   c. They convert ammonia into uric acid.

   d. They form a thick paste that leaves the body through the rectum.

Response (page 756)

17. What three trends do invertebrates show in the evolution of the nervous system?

    a. _____

    b. _____

    c. _____

18. Number the following groups of invertebrates according to how centralized their nervous system is. Number the group with the simplest nervous system *1*.

    _____ **a.** Flatworms

    _____ **b.** Cnidarians

    _____ **c.** Arthropods

19. What is cephalization? _____

    _____

20. Is the following sentence true or false? The more complex an animal's nervous system, the more developed its sense organs are. _____

Movement and Support (pages 756–757)

21. What are the three main kinds of skeletal systems among invertebrates?

    a. _____

    b. _____

    c. _____

22. What invertebrates have endoskeletons? _____

Sexual and Asexual Reproduction (pages 757–758)

23. What is the difference between external and internal fertilization? _____

    _____

    _____

24. Circle the letter of each sentence that is true about invertebrate reproduction.

    a. Most invertebrates reproduce sexually in one part of their life cycle.

    b. Asexual reproduction maintains genetic diversity in a population.

    c. Asexual reproduction includes budding and division in two.

    d. Most invertebrates have separate sexes.

Vocabulary Review

Answering Questions   *In the space provided, write an answer to each question.*

1. Why are events of the early Cambrian Period called the Cambrian Explosion? _____
_____
_____

2. What is the advantage of cephalization? _____
_____
_____

3. What are the two basic features that all respiratory systems share? _____
_____
_____
_____

Matching   *In the space provided, write the letter of the definition that best matches each term.*

_____   4. acoelomate

_____   5. hydrostatic skeleton

_____   6. intracellular digestion

_____   7. internal fertilization

_____   8. deuterostome

_____   9. extracellular digestion

_____ 10. pseudocoelomate

_____ 11. protostome

_____ 12. external fertilization

_____ 13. exoskeleton

_____ 14. coelomate

_____ 15. endoskeleton

a. fertilization inside the body of the female

b. animal whose blastopore develops into its mouth

c. fluid-filled body cavity surrounded and supported by muscles

d. fertilization outside the body of the female

e. animal whose blastopore develops into its anus

f. animal whose body cavity is fully lined with mesoderm

g. animal with no body cavity

h. food is broken down in a digestive cavity or tract

i. hard body covering

j. structural support inside the body

k. animal whose body cavity is partly lined with mesoderm

l. food is broken down within cells

Chapter 29 Comparing Invertebrates   **Section Review 29-1**

Reviewing Key Concepts

Short Answer *On the lines provided, answer the following questions.*

1. As animals became larger and more complex, how were specialized cells grouped to perform complex functions?

   _____

   _____

2. Describe two kinds of body symmetry.

   _____

   _____

3. What is cephalization and how does it affect the way an animal responds to the environment?

   _____

   _____

4. Over the course of evolution, what has happened to the different segments of most invertebrates?

   _____

   _____

5. What is a coelom? What distinguishes a true coelom from a pseudocoelom?

   _____

   _____

6. What are protostomes and deuterosomes? Give an invertebrate example of each.

   _____

   _____

Reviewing Key Skills

7. **Applying Concepts** Explain why there are relatively few fossils dating from before the Cambrian Period.

   _____

   _____

Classifying *On the lines provided, classify each organism as having one of the following types of symmetry:* no symmetry, radial symmetry, *or* bilateral symmetry.

8. _____   9. _____   10. _____

Reviewing Key Concepts

Short Answer *On the lines provided, answer the following questions.*

1. How does the digestive process in simple and complex animals differ?

   _____

   _____

2. Identify the two basic features of all respiratory systems.

   _____

   _____

3. What are the two types of circulatory systems in invertebrates?

   _____

   _____

4. What is the function of an excretory system in animals?

   _____

   _____

5. What three trends do invertebrates show in the evolution of the nervous system?

   _____

   _____

6. Identify the three skeletal systems of invertebrates.

   _____

   _____

7. What are the basic ways that invertebrates reproduce?

   _____

   _____

Reviewing Key Skills

8. **Applying Concepts** How do some insects use Malpighian tubules to maintain water balance?

   _____

   _____

9. **Comparing and Contrasting** What is the advantage of sexual reproduction?

   _____

   _____

Chapter 29 Comparing Invertebrates — Chapter Vocabulary Review

Defining Terms *On the lines provided, write a definition for each of the following terms.*

1. cephalization _____
_____
_____

2. intracellular digestion _____
_____
_____

3. extracellular digestion _____
_____
_____

4. open circulatory system _____
_____
_____

5. closed circulatory system _____
_____
_____

Multiple Choice *On the lines provided, write the letter of the answer that best completes each sentence.*

_____ 6. Invertebrates with mirror-image left and right sides have

    a. bilateral symmetry.   c. unilateral symmetry.

    b. bifunctional symmetry.   d. radial symmetry.

_____ 7. Invertebrates that have no coelom lack a

    a. heart.   c. digestive tract.

    b. body cavity.   d. mouth.

_____ 8. Blood stays within blood vessels in a(an)

    a. open circulatory system.   c. nervous system.

    b. respiratory system.   d. closed circulatory system.

_____ 9. The process of fertilization in which adults release eggs and sperm into surrounding water is called

    a. asexual reproduction.   c. internal fertilization.

    b. asexual fertilization.   d. external fertilization.

_____ 10. The process in which eggs are fertilized inside the body of a female animal is called

    a. internal fertilization.   c. external fertilization.

    b. asexual fertilization.   d. asexual reproduction.

Matching *On the lines provided, write the name of the invertebrate group or groups that exhibit the features described.*

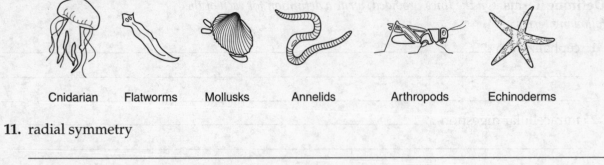

Cnidarian   Flatworms   Mollusks   Annelids   Arthropods   Echinoderms

11. radial symmetry

_____
_____

12. cephalization

_____
_____

13. true coelom

_____
_____

14. protostome development

_____
_____

Completing Tables *In the spaces provided, fill in a description and give two examples of animals with the different types of skeletons.*

	Hydrostatic Skeleton	**Exoskeleton**	**Endoskeleton**
Description	**15.**	**16.**	**17.**
Examples of animals with this type of skeleton	**18.**	**19.**	**20.**

Animals of the Vendian Period

Paleontologists know that life existed in the history of Earth during Precambrian time, which ended about 544 million years ago, but most fossils from this era are of microscopic, unicellular organisms. After some fossil discoveries in South Australia, northern Russia, and a few other locales, paleontologists now know that multicellular, macroscopic animals did exist during the latter part of this era.

Fossils from this period, now known as the Vendian Period (650 to 544 million years ago), are typically impressions left by soft-bodied animals such as *Dickinsonia*. Classifying these fossils, however has been very difficult and the classifications are still open for debate. For example, the organisms that made some of the fossils in the Vendian Period, like *Dickinsonia*, were thought to be algae, lichens, or even giant protozoa. Some of the animals from the Vendian Period may belong to separate kingdoms that are unrelated to any currently living organisms. The most difficult Vendian fossils to interpret are little more than blobs. There is not enough of the animals' shapes left to attempt to classify these fossils. Others somewhat resemble cnidarians like corals or jellyfish. Still others resemble worms.

Fossils from the Vendian Period are not readily available because many Precambrian rock layers are either deeply buried or have been metamorphosed into other rocks by tectonic forces. One area where Vendian fossils can be found is in the Ediacara Hills in the province of South Australia. A mining geologist who was exploring the area discovered these fossils in 1946. Another, perhaps richer, source of Vendian fossils is along the Winter Coast region of Russia. This area borders the White Sea of the Arctic Ocean, and is accessible by boat only during the summer.

Evaluation *On the lines provided, answer the following questions.*

1. Could multicellular animals have existed before the Vendian period? If so, why have paleontologists not found their fossils?

   _____

   _____

   _____

   _____

2. What about Vendian fossils makes them so difficult to identify and classify?

   _____

   _____

   _____

   _____

Chapter 29 Comparing Invertebrates   **Graphic Organizer**

Compare/Contrast Table

Using the information in the chapter, complete the compare/contrast table below which compares three different groups of invertebrates. If there is not enough room in the table to write your answers, write them on a separate sheet of paper.

	Sponges	Arthropods	Echinoderms
Body symmetry	No symmetry	1.	2.
Cephalization	3.	4.	None as adults
Germ layers	5.	Ectoderm, endoderm, and mesoderm	6.
Early Development (protostome or deuterostome)	Neither	7.	8.
Digestion	Intracellular	9.	10.
Circulatory system	None, uses diffusion	11.	None, uses diffusion

Chapter 29 Comparing Invertebrates   **Chapter Test A**

Multiple Choice

Write the letter that best answers the question or completes the statement on the line provided.

_____ 1. Which of the following did NOT occur during the Cambrian Explosion?
   a. Animals acquired specialized cells, tissues, and organ systems.
   b. There was an extraordinary growth in animal diversity.
   c. Animals evolved simpler body plans.
   d. Animal appendages became specialized for a variety of functions.

_____ 2. One characteristic that made early animals different from all animals of today was their
   a. habitat.   c. body plan.
   b. body segmentation.   d. bilateral symmetry.

_____ 3. Animals of the Cambrian Period typically had all of the following EXCEPT
   a. body symmetry.   c. some type of skeleton.
   b. segmentation.   d. a backbone.

_____ 4. The classification of an animal as a deuterostome or a protostome is based on
   a. its body symmetry.
   b. whether or not it has a coelom.
   c. what happens to the blastopore.
   d. the number of germ layers it has.

_____ 5. An acoelomate is an animal that has
   a. a body cavity lined with endoderm and ectoderm.
   b. a body cavity partially lined with mesoderm.
   c. a body cavity completely lined with mesoderm.
   d. no body cavity between the germ layers.

_____ 6. Which invertebrates exhibit radial symmetry?
   a. cnidarians and echinoderms
   b. sponges and flatworms
   c. roundworms and annelids
   d. mollusks and arthropods

_____ 7. Cephalization refers to the
   a. division of the body into upper and lower sides.
   b. concentration of sense organs and nerve cells in the front of the body.
   c. joining together of specialized cells to form tissues.
   d. formation of a body cavity between the germ layers.

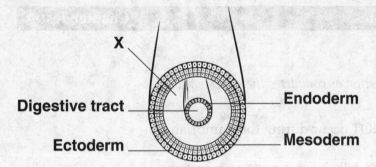

Digestive tract — Endoderm

Ectoderm — Mesoderm

Figure 1

_____ **8.** One animal that has a body construction like that shown in Figure 1 is a
   a. flatworm.   c. sponge.
   b. roundworm.   d. jellyfish.

_____ **9.** In Figure 1, the space labeled X is called a
   a. protostome.
   b. deuterostome.
   c. coelom.
   d. pseudocoelom.

_____ **10.** The distinguishing feature of a closed circulatory system is that
   a. it does not include a heart.
   b. blood is contained within vessels that extend throughout the body.
   c. blood is kept at low pressure.
   d. blood is circulated less efficiently than in an open circulatory system.

_____ **11.** Which structures are NOT part of an excretory system?
   a. flame cells   c. Malpighian tubules
   b. spiracles   d. nephridia

_____ **12.** Which of the following best describes uric acid?
   a. more toxic than ammonia, leaves the body through excretory pores
   b. more toxic than ammonia, leaves the body through the rectum
   c. less toxic than ammonia, leaves the body through excretory pores
   d. less toxic than ammonia, leaves the body through the rectum

_____ **13.** An example of an invertebrate with a hydrostatic skeleton is a(an)
   a. spider.   c. sea star.
   b. sponge.   d. earthworm.

____**14.** An endoskeleton is a

    a. shell of a mollusk.

    b. fluid-filled body cavity that supports the muscles.

    c. structural support located inside the body.

    d. hard body covering made of chitin.

____**15.** Which statement refers to sexual reproduction?

    a. All offspring are genetically identical to the parent.

    b. Offspring are produced from the fusion of male and female gametes.

    c. An organism breaks into pieces that grow into new individuals.

    d. New individuals are produced from outgrowths of the parent's body wall.

Completion

Complete each statement on the line provided.

16. Over the course of evolution, _____ allowed animals to increase in body size with a minimum of new genetic material.

17. Echinoderms differ from cnidarians in that echinoderms develop from three embryonic _____ layers.

18. If an invertebrate has gills, it most likely lives in a(an) _____ environment.

19. The function of a flame cell is to rid the body of excess _____ .

20. If an animal moves by contracting muscles that surround a body cavity filled with fluid, the animal has a(an) _____ skeleton.

Short Answer

In complete sentences, write the answers to the questions on the lines provided.

21. Why are animal fossils more abundant from the Cambrian Period than from earlier periods?

_____

_____

_____

22. Name three invertebrate phyla with bilateral symmetry.

_____

_____

23. Explain the advantage of cephalization.

_____

_____

24. Why must the surfaces of respiratory systems be moist?

_____

_____

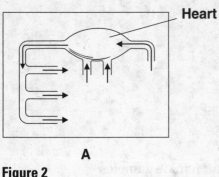

Heart

A

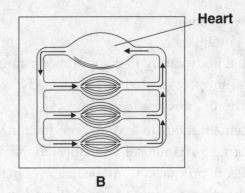

Heart

B

Figure 2

25. Identify each circulatory system in Figure 2 as open or closed.

_____

_____

_____

_____

Using Science Skills

Use the diagram below to answer the questions on the lines provided.

26. Interpreting Graphics Figure 3 shows one theory about the evolutionary relationships among groups of living invertebrates and chordates. Which feature evolved twice during the course of invertebrate evolution?

_____

_____

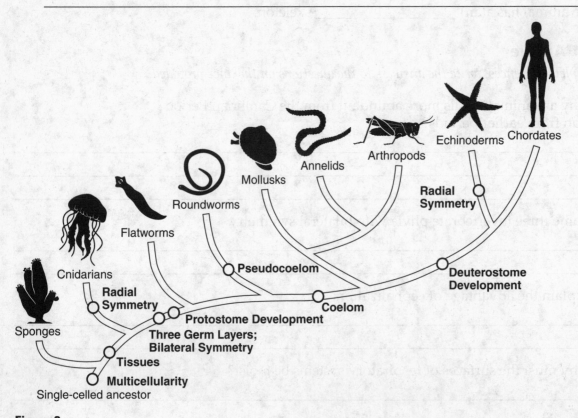

Figure 3

27. **Interpreting Graphics** According to Figure 3, which group(s) of invertebrates develop from three germ layers?

_____

_____

28. **Interpreting Graphics** Look at Figure 3. Which group(s) of invertebrates do NOT have tissues?

_____

29. **Interpreting Graphics** Use Figure 3 to determine to which two groups of invertebrates annelids are most closely related.

_____

30. **Interpreting Graphics** What type of development shown in Figure 3 do mollusks undergo?

_____

Essay

Write the answer to each question in the space provided.

31. Describe the changes in internal specialization that occurred during the evolution of animals.

32. Compare and contrast cnidarians, mollusks, and echinoderms in terms of body symmetry, presence of a body cavity, and cephalization.

33. To remove nitrogenous wastes, some terrestrial invertebrates convert ammonia to urea. Why is that advantageous for these invertebrates? _____

34. Describe the organization of nervous systems in cnidarians, flatworms, and cephalopod mollusks.

35. Contrast hydrostatic skeletons, exoskeletons, and endoskeletons in terms of their structures.

Chapter 29 Comparing Invertebrates

Multiple Choice

Write the letter that best answers the question or completes the statement on the line provided.

____ 1. The diversity of invertebrate phyla underwent its greatest increase
   a. before the Cambrian Period.
   b. during the Cambrian Period.
   c. after the Cambrian Period.

____ 2. Which of the following invertebrates are deuterostomes?
   a. worms
   b. arthropods
   c. echinoderms

____ 3. In a protostome, the blastopore becomes a(an)
   a. mouth.
   b. anus.
   c. zygote.

____ 4. A body cavity that forms between the germ layers is called a(an)
   a. coelom.
   b. blastopore.
   c. mesoderm.

____ 5. Some type of body symmetry is found in all invertebrates EXCEPT
   a. cnidarians.
   b. mollusks.
   c. sponges.

____ 6. During development, a zygote divides repeatedly to form a(an)
   a. endoderm.
   b. endoskeleton.
   c. blastula.

____ 7. Invertebrates that break down their food through intracellular digestion include
   a. annelids.
   b. sponges.
   c. arthropods.

____ 8. Which invertebrate has a gastrovascular cavity?
   a. arthropod
   b. mollusk
   c. cnidarian

_____ **9.** A true digestive tract is found in
  a. annelids.
  b. sponges.
  c. flatworms.

_____**10.** Gases diffuse most efficiently across a respiratory membrane
  if the membrane is
  a. thick and dry
  b. thin and dry.
  c. thin and moist.

_____**11.** In insects, gas exchange takes place through a network of
  a. tracheal tubes.
  b. mantle cavities.
  c. blood vessels.

_____**12.** In an open circulatory system, blood
  a. is pumped through a system of sinuses.
  b. does not come in direct contact with the tissues.
  c. is always contained within a system of blood vessels.

_____**13.** An example of an animal with an open circulatory system is
  a(an)
  a. sponge.
  b. cnidarian.
  c. arthropod.

_____**14.** Which of the following is a function of an excretory system?
  a. eliminating nitrogenous wastes from the body
  b. exchanging oxygen and carbon dioxide with the
     environment
  c. gathering and processing information from the
     environment

_____**15.** The eyespots of flatworms can
  a. detect the presence of light.
  b. detect motion.
  c. detect color.

Completion

Complete each statement on the line provided.

16. _____ fossils are tracks and burrows made by soft-bodied animals
  whose bodies were not fossilized.

17. A body cavity lined partially with mesoderm is called a(an) _____ .

18. The concentration of sense organs and nerve cells in the front of the body is called
  _____ .

Name_____ Class_____ Date _____

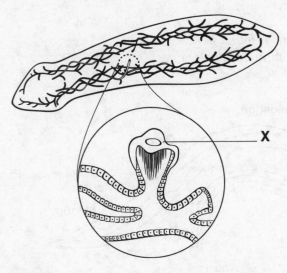

Figure 1

19. Figure 1 shows the excretory system of a flatworm. The structure labeled X is called a(an) _____ .

20. The simplest nervous systems are called _____ .

Short Answer

In complete sentences, write the answers to the questions on the lines provided.

21. What is a blastula?

_____

_____

22. What is the definition of a coelomate?

_____

_____

_____

23. What is intracellular digestion?

_____

_____

_____

24. What are Malpighian tubules?

_____

_____

_____

25. Why must all animals eliminate ammonia from their bodies?

_____

_____

_____

Name_____ Class_____ Date _____

Using Science Skills

The diagram below shows the two types of digestive systems found in invertebrates. Use the diagram to answer the following questions on the lines provided.

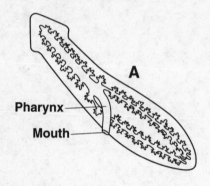 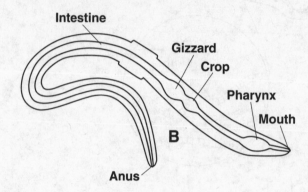

Figure 2

26. **Classifying** Name two phyla of invertebrates that have the type of digestive system shown in A in Figure 2.

_____

27. **Classifying** Name two phyla of invertebrates that have the type of digestive system shown in B in Figure 2.

_____

28. **Applying Concepts** Describe the passage of food through the digestive system shown in A in Figure 2.

_____

_____

_____

_____

29. **Applying Concepts** Describe the passage of food through the digestive system shown in B in Figure 2.

_____

_____

_____

_____

30. **Comparing and Contrasting** What is the difference between intracellular digestion and extracellular digestion?

_____

_____

_____

_____

Multiple Choice

Write the letter that best answers the question or completes the statement on the line provided.

_____ **1.** Each of the following is one of the essential functions animals carry out EXCEPT

    a. respiration.   c. cephalization.

    b. excretion.   d. circulation.

_____ **2.** Which of the following is NOT a reason why sponges are classified as animals?

    a. Sponges are multicellular.

    b. Sponges have no cell walls.

    c. Sponges are heterotrophic.

    d. Sponges are asymmetrical.

_____ **3.** What are the simplest animals to have body symmetry and specialized cells?

    a. flatworms   c. trilobites

    b. sponges   d. cnidarians

_____ **4.** Which of the following is true about corals?

    a. Corals have only the medusa stage in their life cycles.

    b. Coral polyps secrete an underlying skeleton of calcium carbonate.

    c. The polyp form of corals is restricted to a small larval stage.

    d. One coral polyp forms a balloonlike float that keeps the entire colony afloat.

_____ **5.** Which of the following is true about flatworms?

    a. Flatworms are worms with segmented bodies.

    b. Most free-living flatworms reproduce asexually.

    c. All flatworms rely on diffusion for some essential body functions.

    d. Flatworms are unsegmented worms with pseudocoeloms.

_____ **6.** What kind of organism causes the disease trichinosis?

    a. flatworm   c. roundworm

    b. annelid   d. trochophore

_____ **7.** Which of the following is NOT true about earthworms?

    a. Their tunnels allow for the growth of oxygen-requiring soil bacteria.

    b. Earthworms have a pseudocoelom.

    c. Earthworms have a digestive tract that includes a mouth and an anus.

    d. Earthworms are hermaphrodites that reproduce sexually.

_____ **8.** Which of the following describes a mollusk mantle?

    a. a thin layer of tissue that covers most of the body

    b. a system of internal tubes that opens to the outside through a sievelike structure

    c. the segment that contains the brain, eyes, mouth, and legs

    d. the section that consists of the internal organs

_____ **9.** All arthropods have

    a. pedipalps.   c. jointed appendages.

    b. a madreporite.   d. a carapace.

_____ **10.** Which of the following is NOT true about insects?

    a. Insects have a body divided into three parts.

    b. Insects have four pairs of walking legs.

    c. Insects have chemical receptors for taste and smell on their mouthparts.

    d. Insect legs are attached to the thorax.

_____ **11.** What are specific chemical receptors that insects use that affect the behavior or development of other individuals of the same species?

    a. pheromones   c. chelicerae

    b. chitin   d. spiracles

_____ **12.** Which of the following is NOT true about echinoderms?

    a. Most adults exhibit five-part radial symmetry.

    b. The water vascular system carries out many essential body functions.

    c. Echinoderms have an internal skeleton.

    d. The central ring is called the cephalothorax.

_____ **13.** The Burgess Shale animals lived during the

    a. Ediacaran Period.   c. Canadian Period.

    b. Trilobite Period.   d. Cambrian Period.

_____ **14.** Which of the following do NOT exhibit bilateral symmetry?

    a. roundworms   c. cnidarians

    b. mollusks   d. arthropods

_____ **15.** Which of the following is NOT true about complex animals?

    a. Most move blood through their bodies using one or more hearts.

    b. Most have decentralized nervous systems.

    c. Most have a true coelom.

    d. Most use extracellular digestion.

Completion

Complete each statement on the line provided.

16. An animal without a backbone is called a(an)_____.

17. Asexual reproduction in flatworms is by a process

called_____.

18. In a bivalve, water enters and leaves the body through a(an)

_____, a tubelike structure.

19. The process in which an arthropod sheds its exoskeleton and

manufactures a larger one to take its place is _____.

20. The concentration of sense organs and nerve cells in the front of

the body is called _____.

Short Answer

In complete sentences, write the answers to the questions on the lines provided.

21. What are the important evolutionary trends that have occurred in animals as they've become more complex over time?

_____

_____

_____

22. Describe the two stages in the life cycle of a cnidarian.

_____

_____

_____

23. What is the difference between internal fertilization and external fertilization?

_____

_____

_____

24. What are the three major groups of Arthropods?

_____

_____

25. Do echinoderms have a closer evolutionary relationship to mollusks or to chordates? Explain.

_____

_____

_____

Using Science Skills

Use the diagram below to answer the following questions on the lines provided.

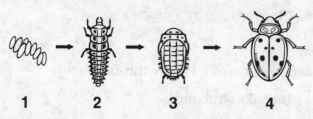

1   2   3   4

Figure 1

26. **Interpreting Graphics** What is the process called that is illustrated in Figure 1? Name three examples of organisms in which the process occurs.

_____

_____

27. **Applying Concepts** What does drawing 1 of Figure 1 represent? Describe the process in which these objects were formed.

_____

_____

_____

28. **Applying Concepts** What does drawing 2 of Figure 1 represent? How is it different from an adult?

_____

_____

_____

29. **Applying Concepts** What does drawing 3 of Figure 1 represent? Describe what occurs at this stage.

_____

_____

_____

30. **Comparing and Contrasting** How is the process shown in Figure 1 like the other form of metamorphosis? How is it different?

_____

_____

_____

_____

Essay

Write the answer to each question in the space provided.

31. Compare the formation of a protostome and a deuterostome.

32. What is the difference between a primary host and an intermediate host? Give an example of each.

33. How are modern arthropods different from primitive arthropods of hundreds of millions of years ago?

34. Describe three types of skeletons found in invertebrates.

35. Describe how terrestrial invertebrates remove nitrogenous wastes from the body.

Multiple Choice

Write the letter that best answers the question or completes the statement on the line provided.

_____ 1. Animals that have no backbone, or vertebral column, are called
   a. vertebrates.
   b. invertebrates.
   c. heterotrophs.

_____ 2. What is a protostome?
   a. an animal whose anus is formed from the blastopore
   b. the outermost germ layer
   c. an animal whose mouth is formed from the blastopore

_____ 3. What is one reason why sponges are classified as animals?
   a. Their cells have cell walls.
   b. Sponges are heterotropic.
   c. Sponges form partnerships with photosynthetic organisms.

_____ 4. Cnidarians have stinging cells called
   a. choanocytes.
   b. flame cells.
   c. cnidocytes.

_____ 5. In flatworms, what structure pumps food into the digestive cavity?
   a. ganglia
   b. gizzard
   c. pharynx

_____ 6. Which of the following describes a pseudocoelom?
   a. body cavity that is lined only partially with mesoderm tissue
   b. body cavity between the mesoderm and the endoderm
   c. body cavity that is fully lined with mesoderm tissue

_____ 7. Which of the following is true about annelids?
   a. Annelids are acoelomates.
   b. Each body segment contains several pairs of antennae.
   c. Annelids have segmented bodies and a true coelom.

_____ 8. Which of the following animals is classified as a cephalopod?
   a. octopus
   b. nudibranch
   c. mussel

_____ **9.** Arthropods have
   a. a soft body and an internal shell.
   b. a segmented body and an exoskeleton.
   c. a flattened body with an external shell.

_____**10.** Which of the following are MOST closely related to spiders?
   a. insects
   b. horseshoe crabs
   c. centipedes

_____**11.** What is a process of changing shape and form that occurs in the development of insects?
   a. cephalization
   b. feedback inhibition
   c. metamorphosis

_____**12.** Which of the following is true about echinoderms?
   a. Most adult echinoderms exhibit radial symmetry.
   b. An echinoderm body is divided into a head, a thorax, and an abdomen.
   c. Echinoderms have one pair of antennae and unbranched appendages.

_____**13.** Which of the following animals are deuterostomes?
   a. cnidarians and mollusks
   b. annelids and arthropods
   c. echinoderms and chordates

_____**14.** Complex animals break down food through the process of
   a. complete metamorphosis.
   b. extracellular digestion.
   c. intracellular digestion.

_____**15.** In terrestrial animals, respiratory surfaces are covered with
   a. layers of chitin.
   b. uric acid.
   c. water or mucus.

Completion

Complete each statement on the line provided.

16. A(An) _____ is an immature stage of an organism that looks different from the adult form.

17. The simplest animal to have bilateral symmetry is a(an) _____.

18. Mollusks called _____ have two shells that are held together by one or two powerful muscles.

19. A spider's two body sections are the abdomen and the _____.

20. Most adult echinoderms exhibit five-part _____ symmetry.

Short Answer

In complete sentences, write the answers to the questions on the lines provided.

21. What are the two stages of a cnidarian called?

_____

_____

22. What are the four parts of a mollusk body plan?

_____

_____

23. What is an open circulatory system?

_____

_____

_____

24. What are the three body sections of an insect? To which section(s) are the legs attached?

_____

_____

_____

25. What is a coelom? Which invertebrate groups have a true coelom?

_____

_____

_____

Name_____ Class_____ Date _____

Using Science Skills

Use the diagram below to answer the following questions on the lines provided.

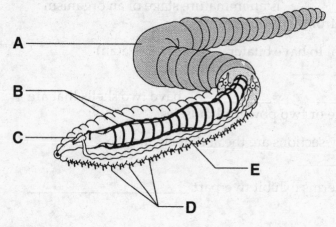

Figure 1

26. **Classifying** What animal is shown in Figure 1?

_____

_____

27. **Interpreting Graphics** Structure A in Figure 1 points to a clitellum. What is the function of the clitellum?

_____

_____

28. **Interpreting Graphics** Structure E is a nerve cord that runs the length of the body. What structure is it attached to, and what is that structure called?

_____

_____

29. **Inferring** Structure B is the dorsal blood vessel, which contains blood that moves from the head to the tail. What type of circulation system does this indicate that the organism has?

_____

_____

30. **Inferring** The structures indicated by D are brushlike structures on the outer surface of the animal. What is the name of these structures, and how could they help as this animal moves?

_____

_____

_____

Chapter 26 Sponges and Cnidarians

Answers for the Adapted Reading and Study Workbook worksheets (pp. 7–14) can be found in the Adapted Reading and Study Workbook, Annotated Teacher's Edition.

Answers for the Reading and Study Workbook worksheets (pp. 17–26) can be found in the Reading and Study Workbook, Annotated Teacher's Edition.

Section Review 26-1

1. multicellular **2.** eukaryotic **3.** cell walls **4.** heterotrophs **5.** Waste products must be excreted because they are toxic. **6.** Sexual reproduction helps create and maintain genetic diversity in populations, perhaps enabling them to evolve when the environment changes. **7.** Complex animals tend to have specialized cells and internal organization. They also have bilateral symmetry, cephalization, and a body cavity. **8.** In both organisms, the blastopore is an opening that becomes a central tube and then a digestive tract. The blastopore of a protostome becomes a mouth. The blastopore of a deuterostome becomes an anus. **9.** Animals with bilateral symmetry have a body that can be divided into two mirror-image halves. They usually have a front and back end and an upper and lower side. Animals with radial symmetry have bodies through which any number of imaginary planes can be drawn, each dividing the body in half. **10.** Usually, a greater degree of cephalization indicates a more complex animal.

Section Review 26-2

1. animal **2.** heterotrophs **3.** do not **4.** some **5.** The movement of water through the sponge enables the sponge to carry out feeding, respiration, circulation, and excretion. **6.** A sponge has collar cells that use flagella to move a current of water through the sponge. **7.** Sponges filter food from water. Digestion is intracellular. **8.** Sponges reproduce sexually when water currents carry the sperm of one sponge to another sponge, where fertilization occurs. In asexual reproduction, part of one sponge breaks off and begins to grow on its own. This is different because no genetic material is exchanged between sponges. **9.** A gemmule can survive difficult conditions that would kill an adult sponge. Later, when the difficult conditions have passed, the gemmule will grow into a new sponge. **10.** Marine animals would lose the shelter they often seek among sponges, so their populations might decrease. Species with whom the sponges formed symbiotic relationships might also see a population decrease.

Section Review 26-3

1.-5. Cnidarians have soft bodies. They are carnivorous. They have stinging tentacles arranged in circles around their mouths. They have body symmetry and specialized tissues. **6.** medusa **7.** polyp **8.** hydras and their relatives; jellyfishes; and sea anemones and corals **9.** Both statocysts and ocelli are groups of sensory cells found in cnidarians. A statocyst helps to determine the direction of gravity, whereas an ocellus detects light. **10.** Possible answer: Sediments eroded by logging, farming, mining, and construction can smother corals. Industrial and agricultural pollutants can poison coral. Overfishing can upset the ecological balance of the reefs.

Chapter Vocabulary Review

1. a **2.** d **3.** e **4.** g **5.** f **6.** i **7.** b **8.** h **9.** c **10.** ectoderm **11.** mesoderm **12.** endoderm **13.** blastopore **14.** spicules; archaeocytes **15.** larva **16.** gemmule **17.** cnidocyte; nematocyst **18.** a **19.** b **20.** b **21.** d **22.** c **23.** a **24.** c **25.** a

Enrichment

1. Gastrozooids specialize in feeding. Others function in reproduction. It also has poisonous stinging cells that subdue prey. **2.** Possible answer: During feeding, cnidocytes subdue prey. The tentacles are responsible for carrying the prey to the gastrozooids, which eat and digest it.

Graphic Organizer

1. gametes (eggs, sperm) **2.** water **3.** Fertilization **4.** larva **5.** polyp **6.** budding

Chapter 26—Test A

Multiple Choice **1.** B **2.** D **3.** C **4.** B **5.** B **6.** B **7.** D **8.** C **9.** A **10.** C **11.** B **12.** B **13.** B **14.** A **15.** B **Completion** **16.** vertebrates **17.** feedback inhibition **18.** anus **19.** gastrovascular cavity **20.** polyp **Short Answer** **21.** A protostome is an animal whose mouth is formed from the blastopore. A deuterostome is an animal whose anus is formed from the blastopore. **22.** Complex animals tend to have high levels of cell specialization and internal body organization, bilateral symmetry, a front end or head with sense organs, and a body cavity. **23.** Cephalization is the concentration of sense organs and nerve cells at the front end of the body. An advantage is that an animal with cephalization can respond to the environment more quickly and in more complex ways than a simpler animal can. **24.** Scyphozoans, such as jellyfishes, live their lives primarily as medusas. A medusa has a motile, bell-shaped body with its mouth on the bottom. **25.** As colonies of coral polyps grow, they secrete an underlying skeleton of calcium carbonate that can build up for thousands of years, forming a coral reef. **Using Science Skills** **26.** Sponges are placed in the phylum Porifera, which means "pore-bearers." This name is appropriate because sponges have tiny openings, or pores, all over their bodies. **27.** A; The osculum is the large hole through which water exits the central cavity of a sponge. **28.** F; Archaeocytes complete the digestive process and transport digested food throughout the sponge. **29.** structure C, which is a choanocyte **30.** Structure B is a spicule, which functions like a lens or a magnifying glass. Spicules focus and direct incoming sunlight to cells lying below the surface of the sponge, where symbiotic organisms carry out photosynthesis. **Essay** **31.** During early development, the cells of most animal embryos differentiate into three germ layers. The endoderm, the innermost germ layer, gives rise to the linings of the digestive tract and much of the respiratory system. The mesoderm, the middle layer, gives rise to muscles and much of the circulatory, reproductive, and excretory systems. The ectoderm, the outermost layer, gives rise to sense organs, nerves, and the outer layer of skin. **32.** Sample answer: A dog exhibits bilateral symmetry, with distinct right and left sides. A dog has pronounced cephalization, and its anterior end is called its head, where the sense organs for sight, smell, hearing, and taste are concentrated. At the posterior end a dog has a tail. A dog's dorsal side is called its back, and its ventral side is called its belly. **33.** A body cavity is important because it provides a space in which internal organs can be suspended, allows for specialized regions to develop, and provides room for internal organs to grow and expand. In some animals, body cavities contain fluids involved in circulation, feeding, and excretion. **34.** Gemmules are groups of archaeocytes surrounded by a tough layer of spicules. Gemmules can survive long periods of freezing temperature and drought. When conditions again become favorable, gemmules can grow into new sponges. In budding, part of the sponge breaks off the parent plant, settles onto the sea floor, and grows into a new sponge. **35.** Cnidarians are predatory carnivores. They are able to capture prey by paralyzing it with stinging nematocysts. Once a cnidarian's prey is paralyzed, it uses its tentacles to push the prey through its mouth and into its gastrovascular cavity, where it is digested.

Chapter 26—Test B

Multiple Choice **1.** C **2.** C **3.** A **4.** A **5.** B **6.** A **7.** B **8.** B **9.** C **10.** C **11.** C **12.** B **13.** A **14.** A **15.** C **Completion** **16.** invertebrates **17.** feedback **18.** deuterostomes **19.** larva **20.** cnidocytes **Short Answer** **21.** feeding, respiration, circulation, excretion, response, movement, and reproduction **22.** The endoderm is the innermost layer, the mesoderm is the middle layer, and the ectoderm is the outermost layer. **23.** Cephalization is the concentration of sense organs and nerve cells at the front end of an animal's body. **24.** The movement of water through a sponge provides a simple mechanism for feeding, respiration, circulation, and excretion. **25.** A polyp has a cylindrical body, tentacles, and a mouth that opens upward. **Using Science Skills** **26.** B **27.** swimming larva **28.** asexually **29.** medusa **30.** Hydras spend their entire lives as polyps. Figure 26-1 includes a medusa stage.

Chapter 27 Worms and Mollusks

Answers for the Adapted Reading and Study Workbook worksheets (pp. 51–58) can be found in the Adapted Reading and Study Workbook, Annotated Teacher's Edition.

Answers for the Reading and Study Workbook worksheets (pp. 61–72) can be found in the Reading and Study Workbook, Annotated Teacher's Edition.

Section Review 27-1

1. organ **2.** germ **3.** bilateral **4.** cephalization **5.** Turbellarians **6.** Flukes **7.** Tapeworms **8.** The thin shape of a flatworm's body places most of its cells close to the external environment. Therefore, materials can diffuse easily between the worm's body and the external environment. **9.** If people walk barefoot, the skin on the lower parts of their feet is exposed. Therefore, it is more likely that *Schistosoma* larvae will be able to penetrate the skin. **10.** A human can become infected with tapeworms if he or she eats undercooked meat that contains the cyst form of the tapeworm. The cysts then mature into adult tapeworms in the human's intestines.

Section Review 27-2

1. unsegmented **2.** pseudocoelom **3.** mouth **4.** anus **5.** c **6.** b **7.** d **8.** b **9.** Avoiding eating meat contaminated with *Trichinella* cysts—and cooking all meat thoroughly—is the best way to interrupt the transmission of the disease. **10.** eggs **11.** small intestine **12.** lungs **13.** swallowed **14.** small intestine **15.** Eggs

Section Review 27-3

1. segmented **2.** mesoderm **3.** closed **4.** setae, segment **5.** Oligochaetes live in soil or fresh water and have only a few setae. **6.** Leeches are external parasites that feed on the blood and body fluids of their host. **7.** Polychaetes are marine annelids with pairs of paddlelike appendages, each of which carries setae. **8.** Longitudinal muscles can contract to make the worm shorter and fatter. In contrast, circular muscles can contract to make the worm longer and thinner. **9.** In the past, leeches were used as a possible cure for many ailments. Now, leeches are used for a few applications to which they are well suited; for example, reducing swelling after surgeries in which a body part is reattached, and to prevent blood from clotting. **10.** Earthworms aerate the soil, provide passageways for plant roots and water, bring minerals from deeper in the soil to the surface, fertilize the soil with their feces, and decompose soil.

Section Review 27-4

1. Mollusks are soft-bodied animals that usually have an internal or external shell. **2.** Gastropods are shell-less or single-shelled mollusks that move using a muscular ventral foot. **3.** Bivalves are mollusks with two shells held together by one or two powerful muscles. **4.** Cephalopods are soft-bodied mollusks with a head attached to a single foot that is divided into tentacles or arms. **5.** The shell protects the body of the mollusk. **6.** The visceral mass contains the internal organs. **7.** The mantle covers most of the mollusk's body and secretes the material that makes up the shell. **8.** The foot may function in moving, burrowing, and catching prey. **9.** Fast motion requires more energy than slower motion; a closed circulatory system is more efficient at delivering the oxygen and nutrients used to produce that energy. **10.** Some mollusks concentrate pollutants and microorganisms in their tissues. Scientists can check the levels of pollutants in mollusk tissue to monitor the level of pollutants in the environment in which the mollusks are found.

Chapter Vocabulary Review

1. c **2.** a **3.** a **4.** b **5.** b **6.** c **7.** d **8.** d **9.** b **10.** b **11.** A flatworm extends its pharynx out of its mouth and pumps food into its gastrovascular cavity. **12.** A hermaphrodite has both male and female sex organs. **13.** An adult tapeworm uses its scolex to attach to the intestinal wall of its host. **14.** Septa are internal walls found between the segments of an annelid's body. **15.** closed circulatory system **16.** Nephridia are specialized excretory organs that help eliminate nitrogen by filtering fluid in the coelom. **17.** During reproduction, the clitellum secretes a mucus ring into which eggs and sperm are released. **18.** A trochophore is a free-swimming larval stage of some mollusks and annelids. **19.** Snails use a tongue-shaped radula to feed. **20.** An octopus uses a siphon to propel itself through water.

Enrichment

1. No, you probably would not know the leech was there due to the anesthetic in the leech's saliva.

2. A leech respires through its skin, so a flattened body provides a greater surface area for respiration.

Graphic Organizer

1. Flatworms **2.** Roundworms **3.** Two openings **4.** Two openings **5.** Turbellarians **6.** Tapeworms **7.** Free-living worms **8.** Oligochaetes **9.** Polychaetes

Chapter 27—Test A

Multiple Choice **1.** A **2.** C **3.** D **4.** B **5.** B **6.** C **7.** B **8.** D **9.** C **10.** C **11.** B **12.** D **13.** B **14.** B **15.** A **Completion** **16.** mesoderm **17.** hermaphrodite **18.** gizzard **19.** polychaetes **20.** foot **Short Answer** **21.** by removing remnants of feces that might contain ascarid eggs **22.** A roundworm has a pseudocoelom, which is a cavity formed between the endoderm and mesoderm layers but only partially lined with mesoderm tissue. Annelids have a true coelom, a cavity lined with tissue derived from the mesoderm. **23.** Earthworm feces fertilize the soil; earthworms also mix and aerate the soil, providing passageways for roots and water and allowing the growth of beneficial bacteria. **24.** As water passes through the mantle cavity, oxygen and carbon dioxide diffuse over the animal's gills. **25.** Students should mention any three examples for each class: Gastropoda, which includes pond snails, land slugs, sea butterflies, sea hares, limpets, and nudibranchs; Bivalvia, which includes clams, oysters, mussels, and scallops; and Cephalopoda, which includes octopi, squids, cuttlefishes, and nautiluses. **Using Science Skills** **26.** The organism is an earthworm, of the class Oligochaeta and the phylum Annelid. **27.** Structure A is a clitellum. When eggs are ready for fertilization, it secretes a mucous ring into which eggs and sperm are released. Fertilization takes place in the mucous ring. **28.** Structure B is the dorsal blood vessel, through which blood moves from head to tail. **29.** The structures labeled D are setae, which help an earthworm prevent slippage as it moves. **30.** Structure C is the brain. Attached to the brain is structure E, a nerve cord. Both are parts of a well-developed nervous system. **Essay** **31.** A blood fluke matures and reproduces sexually in the blood vessels of human intestines. Fluke embryos are released and pass out of the human body with feces. If they get into the water, embryos develop into swimming larvae that infect freshwater snails, the intermediate host. In snails, flukes reproduce asexually, and new larvae are released into the water. They then infect humans, the primary host, by burrowing through the skin. **32.** Many flatworms rely on diffusion to remove wastes from their bodies. Some flatworms have a network of flame cells that empties metabolic wastes such as ammonia and urea from the body into the outside environment. In annelids, digestive waste passes out through the anus at the end of the digestive tract. Cellular waste containing nitrogen is eliminated by nephridia, which are excretory organs that filter fluid in the coelom. **33.** A trochophore is a free-swimming larva. Since both mollusks and annelids have trochophore larvae, those groups may be closely related. **34.** They circulate water through their body cavities using currents created by cilia on their gills. Food particles in the water are trapped by mucus and cilia on the gills. **35.** In an open circulatory system, blood is pumped through vessels by a simple heart. Blood eventually leaves the vessels and works its way through different sinuses, which are large saclike spaces. The blood passes from the sinuses to the gills, where oxygen and carbon dioxide are exchanged, and then back to the heart. Mollusks have an open circulatory system. In a closed circulatory system, blood is contained within a network of blood vessels. Annelids have a closed circulatory system.

Chapter 27—Test B

Multiple Choice   **1.** B **2.** A **3.** B **4.** A **5.** A **6.** A
7. B **8.** B **9.** C **10.** C **11.** A **12.** C **13.** A **14.** A **15.** B
Completion   **16.** flatworms **17.** carnivores **18.** closed
19. mesoderm **20.** tentacles **Short Answer**
21. Flatworms are soft, flattened worms with tissues, organ systems, three germ layers, bilateral symmetry, and cephalization. **22.** Snails are intermediate hosts, in which the blood fluke reproduces asexually. **23.** The inner tube is the digestive tract, and the outer tube is the body wall. **24.** Hookworms develop in the soil and can enter the body through the unprotected skin of a human. **25.** foot, mantle, shell, and visceral mass   **Using Science Skills**
26. Planarian (however accept flatworm as well)
27. D, pharynx **28.** ganglia **29.** A, eyespot **30.** Its body is thin, making most of its cells close to the external environment.

Chapter 28 Arthropods and Echinoderms

Answers for the Adapted Reading and Study Workbook worksheets (pp. 98–106) can be found in the Adapted Reading and Study Workbook, Annotated Teacher's Edition.

Answers for the Reading and Study Workbook worksheets (pp. 109–120) can be found in the Reading and Study Workbook, Annotated Teacher's Edition.

Section Review 28-1

1.-3. Arthropods have segmented bodies. Their bodies are surrounded by an exoskeleton. They have jointed appendages. **4.** Arthropods have developed fewer body segments during the course of evolution. **5.** Arthropods have developed more specialized appendages for feeding, movement, and other functions during the process of evolution.
6. The function of molting is to allow arthropods room for growth. When it molts, an arthropod sheds its entire exoskeleton and manufactures another larger exoskeleton to take its place. **7.** A waxy coating prevents water loss in terrestrial arthropods. This allows the arthropod to retain the moisture in its body and therefore helps it survive on land. **8.** Book lungs and tracheal tubes are different means of respiration used by terrestrial arthropods. Book lungs are organs filled with layers of respiratory tissue arranged like the pages of a book. Tracheal tubes form a system of branching air-filled tubes that extend throughout the body. **9.** Terrestrial arthropods use Malpighian tubules to move wastes from the bloodstream to the gut where they are expelled with feces. In aquatic arthropods, diffusion moves cellular waste from the body into the surrounding water. **10.** The muscles of arthropods generate force by contracting and then transfer that force to the exoskeleton. At each joint there are different muscles that flex and extend the joint.

Section Review 28-2

1. body segments **2.** mouthparts **3.** a **4.** b **5.** a **6.** c
7. c **8.** b **9.** c **10.** b **11.** b **12.** The flipperlike structure of the swimmerets enables them to function like paddles and push the crayfish through the water.
13. A spider uses the first pair of appendages, called chelicerae, to capture and paralyze prey. The second pair of appendages, called pedipalps, are used to handle prey. **14.** A spider does not have jaws and must liquefy its food before eating it. So, a spider will inject digestive enzymes into its captured prey and then wait for these enzymes to break down the tissues of its prey. **15.** Millipedes feed on dead or decaying plant material. Venom would be useless, because venom is used to paralyze and kill animals.

Section Review 28-3

1. head, thorax, abdomen **2.** thorax **3.** Larvae
4. societies **5.** complete metamorphosis
6. incomplete metamorphosis **7.** A moth's mouthpart consists of a long tubelike structure that can go deep inside flowers to suck the nectar out of the flower. **8.** No. Pheromones only affect animals of the same species as the animals that release them.
9. Depending on the species, insects may use pheromones, visual cues, or sounds to attract mates.

10. When a honeybee finds a food source that is near the hive, the bee uses a round dance in the hive to communicate this information to the other bees. The dance would include frequent changes in direction to indicate a food source of great energy value.

Section Review 28-4

1.-5. Five characteristics of echinoderms are: spiny skin, radial symmetry, an internal skeleton, a water vascular system, and suction cuplike structures called tube feet. **6.** Three essential body functions carried out by the water vascular system are respiration, circulation, and movement. **7.** Sea urchins and sand dollars; brittle stars; sea cucumbers; sea stars and sea lilies and feather stars are the major classes of echinoderms. **8.** Despite the fact that both cnidarians and adult echinoderms exhibit radial symmetry, echinoderms are actually more closely related to chordates. Both chordates and echinoderms are deuterostomes. **9.** Muscles pull on the sucker at the end of the tube foot, forming a cup shape and producing a partial vacuum that allows the foot to hold on to an object. **10.** Both sea stars and sea lilies use tube feet for feeding. However, a sea star might use its tube feet to pry open a mollusk, whereas a sea lily would use its tube feet to capture plankton floating in the water.

Chapter Vocabulary Review

1. d **2.** f **3.** e **4.** g **5.** c **6.** b **7.** a **8.** cephalothorax **9.** abdomen **10.** swimmeret **11.** carapace **12.** cheliped **13.** mandible **14.** b **15.** c **16.** b **17.** a **18.** d **19.** tracheal tubes **20.** pedipalps **21.** society **22.** caste **23.** water vascular system **24.** madreporite **25.** tube foot

Enrichment

1. Most ants are females. Most female ants are wingless workers that develop from fertilized eggs and are specialized to perform one of many tasks required to maintain the colony. A few ants are winged males that develop from unfertilized eggs and live only to mate with the queen ant. **2.** Leafcutter ants grow their own food, a fungus, and must excavate chambers that are moist enough to grow the fungus on the leaves. Harvester ants eat seeds and must excavate large chambers to store the seeds.

Graphic Organizer

1. Crustaceans **2.** Uniramians **3.** Spiders, horseshoe crabs, ticks, mites, scorpions **4.** Two: cephalothorax and abdomen **5.** Chelicerae and pedipalps **6.** Mandibles **7.** Jaws **8.** Two pairs **9.** One pair **10.** Usually four pairs

Chapter 28—Test A

Multiple Choice **1.** C **2.** C **3.** A **4.** B **5.** A **6.** D **7.** C **8.** D **9.** B **10.** D **11.** A **12.** A **13.** C **14.** D **15.** C **Completion** **16.** nerve cord **17.** crustacean **18.** pedipalps **19.** chelicerae **20.** water vascular **Short Answer** **21.** insect: head, thorax, abdomen; chelicerate: cephalothorax, abdomen **22.** Spiders use book lungs. **23.** Insects pollinate crops; produce commercially valuable products such as silk, wax, and honey; and are eaten by humans. **24.** Stage 1: eggs, Stage 2: larva, Stage 3: pupa, Stage 4: adult **25.** Echinoderms are bilaterally symmetrical as larvae but radially symmetrical as adults. **Using Science Skills** **26.** The animal has radial symmetry demonstrated by the centrally located ring canal, the arms, and internal structures, which are arranged around the central body. **27.** the stomach; To feed, a sea star pushes its stomach out through its mouth, pours out enzymes, and digests its food. When the sea star has finished feeding, it pulls its stomach back into its mouth. **28.** Structure 2 is the madreporite, structure 3 is the ring canal, and structure 4 is a radial canal. **29.** tube feet; when water is pushed into them, they expand. When water is pulled out, the cups on their ends shrink, creating a partial vacuum that holds them to whatever they are touching and allows the animal to walk. **30.** The tube feet use suction to pull open shelled prey. **Essay** **31.** Skin glands digest the inner part of the exoskeleton, and other glands secrete a new skeleton. The animal pulls itself out of what remains of the original skeleton. While the new exoskeleton is still soft, the animal fills with air or fluids to allow room for growth before the next molting. **32.** Spiders have two body sections, whereas insects have three. Spiders have four pairs of legs, whereas insects have three. Spiders lack antennae, whereas insects have one pair. Spiders have two pairs of appendages that are used as mouthparts, whereas insects have three pairs, including a pair of mandibles. **33.** Both centipedes and millipedes are uniramians. They both have jaws, one pair of antennae, unbranched appendages, and a highly segmented body. Both live under rocks. Centipedes have one pair of legs on most body segments, whereas millipedes have two pairs. Centipedes eat other animals, whereas millipedes eat dead and decaying plant material. **34.** The bee runs forward in a straight line while waggling her abdomen. She then circles around one way, runs in a straight line again, and circles around the other way. The farther away the food is, the longer the bee takes to perform the straight run and the more she waggles. The direction of the straight run indicates the direction of the food. **35.** Sperm are produced in testes, and eggs are produced in ovaries. Both types of gametes are shed into the water, where fertilization takes place. The larvae, which have bilateral symmetry, swim around for some time and then swim to the ocean bottom, where they develop into radially symmetrical adults.

Chapter 28—Test B

Multiple Choice **1.** A **2.** C **3.** C **4.** B **5.** C **6.** A **7.** A **8.** C **9.** A **10.** B **11.** B **12.** B **13.** C **14.** B **15.** A **Completion** **16.** segments **17.** chitin **18.** fangs **19.** three **20.** castes **Short Answer** **21.** a segmented body, a tough exoskeleton, and jointed appendages **22.** crustaceans or chelicerates **23.** Mites and ticks are often parasites; they may cause itching or rashes and can transmit bacteria that cause diseases. **24.** complete metamorphosis **25.** Each piece will grow into a new animal, as long as it contains a portion of the central part of the body. **Using Science Skills** **26.** 6 mm (12 mm – 6 mm) during the first molt and by 8 mm (20 mm – 12 mm) during the second molt **27.** While its new exoskeleton was still soft, the arthropod expanded its body by filling with air or fluids. **28.** 12 mm **29.** The exoskeleton of an arthropod is inflexible, so an arthropod cannot grow between molts. **30.** 14 days

Chapter 29 Comparing Invertebrates

Answers for the Adapted Reading and Study Workbook worksheets (pp. 144–152) can be found in the Adapted Reading and Study Workbook, Annotated Teacher's Edition.

Answers for the Reading and Study Workbook worksheets (pp. 155–162) can be found in the Reading and Study Workbook, Annotated Teacher's Edition.

Section Review 29-1

1. Specialized cells were grouped in tissues, organs, and organ systems to perform complex functions. **2.** Animals with bilateral symmetry have mirror-image left and right sides. Radial symmetry exists when the body parts of an organism extend from the center of its body. **3.** Cephalization is a concentration of sense organs and nerve cells in the front of a body. This allows a quicker and more sophisticated response to the environment. **4.** The different segments of most invertebrates have become specialized for specific functions. **5.** A coelom is a body cavity. A true coelom is lined completely with mesoderm. A pseudocoelom is lined only partially with mesoderm. **6.** A protostome is an animal whose blastopore develops into a mouth in its early development. A

deuterostome organism is one that has its blastopore develop into an anus. An invertebrate example of a protostome is an arthropod and a deuterostome example is an enchinoderm. **7.** Prior to the Cambrian Period, most organisms had soft bodies, which generally were not preserved as fossils. **8.** radial symmetry **9.** bilateral symmetry **10.** no symmetry

Section Review 29-2

1. Simple animals break down food primarily through intracellular digestion. Complex animals break down food through extracellular digestion. **2.** All respiratory organs have large surface areas that are in contact with air or water, and moist surfaces for diffusion to occur. **3.** closed circulatory system, open circulatory system **4.** The excretory system in animals rids the body of metabolic waste and maintains water balance. **5.** centralization, cephalization, and specialization. **6.** hydrostatic skeleton, exoskeleton, and endoskeleton **7.** Most invertebrates reproduce sexually during part of their life cycle. Many invertebrates may also reproduce asexually depending on environmental conditions. **8.** Some insects use Malpighian tubes to convert ammonia to uric acid, which is excreted as a paste. This process reduces the water loss of a grasshopper. **9.** Sexual reproduction maintains genetic diversity in a population by creating individuals with new combinations of genes.

Chapter Vocabulary Review

1. Cephalization is the concentration of sense organs and nerve cells in the front of an animal's body. **2.** Intracellular digestion occurs inside cells, and nutrients are passed to other cells by diffusion. **3.** Extracellular digestion occurs outside of cells in a digestive tract; nutrients are then absorbed into the body. **4.** An open circulatory system is one in which blood is not confined within blood vessels, but instead is pumped from the blood vessels into a system of sinuses. **5.** In a closed circulatory system, blood stays within blood vessels that extend throughout the body. **6.** a **7.** b **8.** d **9.** d **10.** a **11.** cnidarians and echinoderms **12.** flatworms, mollusks, annelids, and arthropods **13.** arthropods, mollusks, annelids, and echinoderms **14.** flatworms, mollusks, annelids, and arthropods **15.** A hydrostatic skeleton is a skeleton in which muscles surround a fluid-filled body cavity that supports the muscles; when the muscles contract, they push against the body cavity, causing it to change shape. **16.** An exoskeleton is a hard external body covering. **17.** An endoskeleton is a structural support located inside the body. **18.** cnidarians and earthworms **19.** mollusks and arthropods **20.** echinoderms

Enrichment

1. It is possible that multicellular animals existed before the Vendian Period. Like the Vendian animals, earlier animals may have been soft-bodied, so they did not leave fossils. Or, paleontologists simply may not yet have found any earlier fossils. **2.** The fact that Vendian animals were soft-bodied makes their fossils hard to identify. There often is not much detail in the fossils.

Graphic Organizer

1. Bilateral **2.** Radial **3.** None **4.** Present **5.** None **6.** Ectoderm, endoderm, and mesoderm **7.** Protostome **8.** Deuterostome **9.** Extracellular **10.** Extracellular **11.** Open circulatory system

Chapter 29—Test A

Multiple Choice   1. C **2.** C **3.** D **4.** C **5.** D **6.** A **7.** B **8.** B **9.** D **10.** B **11.** B **12.** D **13.** D **14.** C **15.** B **Completion   16.** segmentation **17.** germ **18.** aquatic **19.** water **20.** hydrostatic **Short Answer   21.** Some animals of the Cambrian period had shells, skeletons, and other hard body parts, which are well preserved in fossils. **22.** Accept any three of the following: flatworms, roundworms, annelids, mollusks, and arthropods. **23.** Cephalization allows an animal to respond to the environment more quickly and in more sophisticated ways. **24.** Gases diffuse most efficiently across a moist membrane. **25.** A—open, B—closed **Using Science Skills   26.** radial symmetry **27.** flatworms, roundworms, mollusks, annelids, arthropods, and echinoderms **28.** sponges **29.** mollusks and arthropods **30.** protostome development **Essay 31.** Early animals had little internal specialization. They carried out essential functions using specialized cells or simple tissues. As animals became larger and more complex, specialized cells joined together to form tissues, organs, and organ systems. **32.** Cnidarians and echinoderms have radial symmetry; mollusks have bilateral symmetry. Cnidarians have no body cavity or cephalization; mollusks and echinoderms have a true coelom and cephalization. **33.** Terrestrial invertebrates must conserve body water while removing nitrogenous wastes. Urea is much less toxic than ammonia, so it can be concentrated by the excretory system without posing a danger to the animal. Concentrating urea conserves body water. **34.** Cnidarians have nerve nets, which consist of individual nerve cells that form a netlike arrangement throughout the animal's body. Flatworms have a few small clumps of nerve tissue, or ganglia, in the head. Cephalopod mollusks have ganglia that are organized into a brain, which controls and coordinates the nervous system.

35. Hydrostatic skeletons are fluid-filled body cavities surrounded by muscles. Exoskeletons are external skeletons, such as arthropods' hard body covering made of chitin. Endoskeletons are structural supports located inside the body.

Chapter 29—Test B

Multiple Choice   1. B **2.** D **3.** A **4.** A **5.** C **6.** C **7.** B **8.** C **9.** A **10.** C **11.** A **12.** A **13.** C **14.** A **15.** A **Completion   16.** Trace **17.** pseudocoelom **18.** cephalization **19.** flame cell **20.** nerve nets **Short Answer   21.** a hollow ball of cells formed when a zygote undergoes a series of cell divisions **22.** an animal that has a true coelom, or body cavity lined completely with mesoderm **23.** digestion of food inside cells **24.** saclike organs that convert ammonia into uric acid **25.** Ammonia is toxic. **Using Science Skills   26.** cnidarians and flatworms **27.** Accept any two of the following: roundworms, annelids, mollusks, arthropods, and echinoderms. **28.** Food enters and leaves the body through a single opening. Some cells in the gastrovascular cavity secrete enzymes and absorb the digested food. Digested food then diffuses to cells throughout the body. **29.** Food enters the digestive tract through the mouth; passes through the pharynx, crop, gizzard, and intestine; and undigested food leaves through the anus. **30.** In intracellular digestion, food is digested inside of cells. In extracellular digestion, food is broken down outside the cells in a digestive cavity and then absorbed into the body.

Unit 8—Test A

Multiple Choice   1. C **2.** D **3.** D **4.** B **5.** C **6.** A **7.** B **8.** A **9.** C **10.** B **11.** A **12.** D **13.** D **14.** C **15.** B **Completion   16.** invertebrate **17.** fission **18.** siphon **19.** molting **20.** cephalization **Short Answer   21.** Complex animals tend to have high levels of cell specialization and internal body organization, bilateral body symmetry, cephalization, and a body cavity. **22.** A polyp has a sessile, cylindrical body with armlike tentacles, with the mouth pointing upward. A medusa has a motile, bell-shaped body with the mouth on the bottom. **23.** Internal fertilization takes place inside the animal's body. External fertilization takes place outside the body. **24.** Crustaceans, spiders and their relatives, and insects and their relatives (Crustacea, Chelicerata, Uniramia). **25.** Echinoderms have a closer evolutionary relationship to chordates than to mollusks. Both echinoderms and chordates are deuterostomes, whereas mollusks are protostomes.

Using Science Skills 26. The process is complete metamorphosis. Bees, moths, and beetles undergo this process. **27.** Drawing 1 represents the insect's eggs, which are formed through internal fertilization during sexual reproduction. **28.** Drawing 2 represents a larva, which looks and acts nothing like the parents. Larvae typically feed voraciously and grow rapidly. They molt several times but change little in appearance. **29.** Drawing 3 represents a pupa. During the pupal stage, the body is completely remodeled inside and out. **30.** The other form, called incomplete metamorphosis, is much less dramatic. The immature form, called a nymph, looks very much like an adult, and there is a gradual change from nymph to adult. **Essay 31.** In a developing embryo, the blastopore leads into a central tube that runs the length of the embryo. The tube becomes the digestive tract and is formed in one of two ways. A protostome is an animal whose mouth is formed from the blastopore. A deuterostome is an animal whose anus is formed from the blastopore. **32.** During the life cycle, a parasitic organism lives in multiple hosts. In the primary host, the organism reproduces sexually. In the intermediate host, the organism reproduces asexually. **33.** The evolution of arthropods has led to fewer body segments and highly specialized appendages for feeding, movement, and other functions. A typical primitive arthropod was composed of many identical segments. Most living arthropods have only two or three segments, and modern arthropod appendages include antennae, claws, walking legs, wings, flippers, mouthparts, and tails. **34.** A hydrostatic skeleton consists of muscles surrounding a fluid-filled body cavity that supports the muscles. When the muscles contract, they push against the body cavity, causing the body to change shape. An exoskeleton is a tough external covering. An endoskeleton is an internal skeleton. **35.** Terrestrial invertebrates must conserve water while removing nitrogenous wastes from the body. To do this, many animals convert ammonia into a compound called urea, which is less toxic than ammonia. Urea is eliminated from the body in urine, which is highly concentrated. Some insects and arachnids have Malphighian tubules, saclike organs that convert ammonia into uric acid. The uric acid and digestive wastes combine to form a thick paste that leaves the body through the rectum. This paste contains little water.

Unit 8—Test B

Multiple Choice 1. B **2.** C **3.** B **4.** C **5.** C **6.** A **7.** C **8.** A **9.** B **10.** B **11.** C **12.** A **13.** C **14.** B **15.** C **Completion 16.** larva **17.** flatworm **18.** bivalves **19.** cephalothorax **20.** radial **Short Answer 21.** polyp and medusa **22.** foot, mantle, shell, visceral mass **23.** An open circulatory system is one in which blood is pumped through vessels into sinuses. **24.** An insect's three body sections are the head, the thorax, and the abdomen. The legs are attached to the thorax. **25.** A coelom is a fluid-filled body cavity that is lined with tissue derived from the mesoderm. Invertebrates that have a true coelom include annelids, mollusks, arthropods, and echinoderms. **Using Science Skills 26.** earthworm **27.** The clitellum is a band of thickened, specialized segments. The clitellum secretes a mucus ring into which eggs and sperm are released. Fertilization takes place in this ring. **28.** C; brain **29.** closed circulatory system **30.** The structures are setae, which prevent slipping as the animal moves.

Flowchart

Topic:

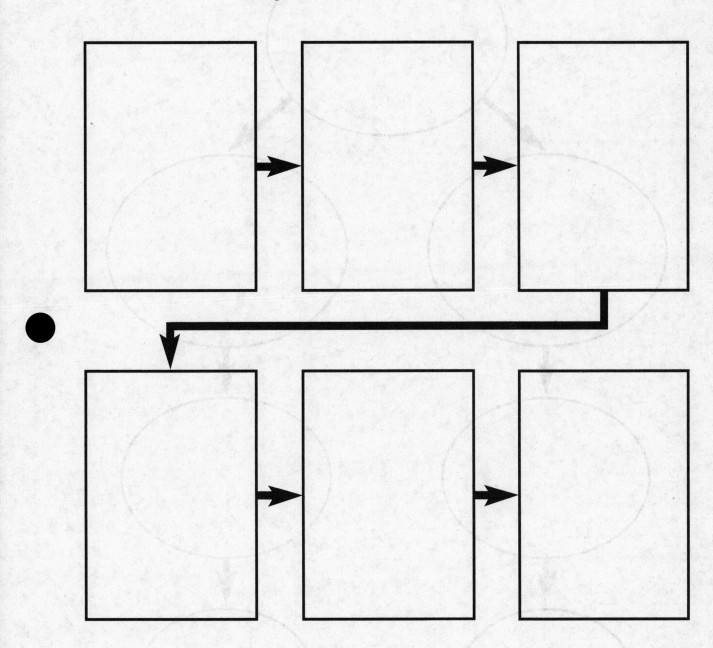

Modified Concept Map

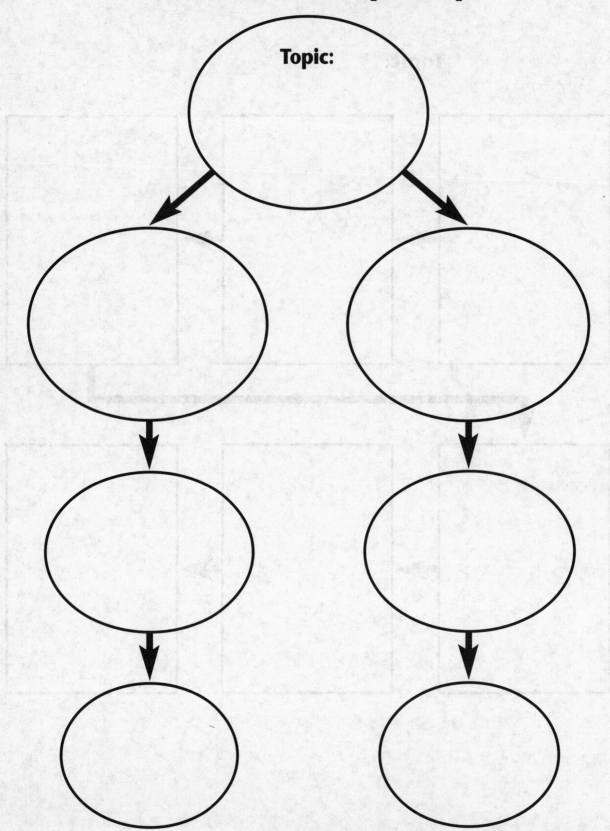

Topic:

Cause/Effect Chart

Topic:

Cause	Effect

Name_____ Class_____ Date _____

Compare/Contrast Chart

Topic:

Similarities	Differences

Venn Diagram

Topic: _____   **Topic:** _____

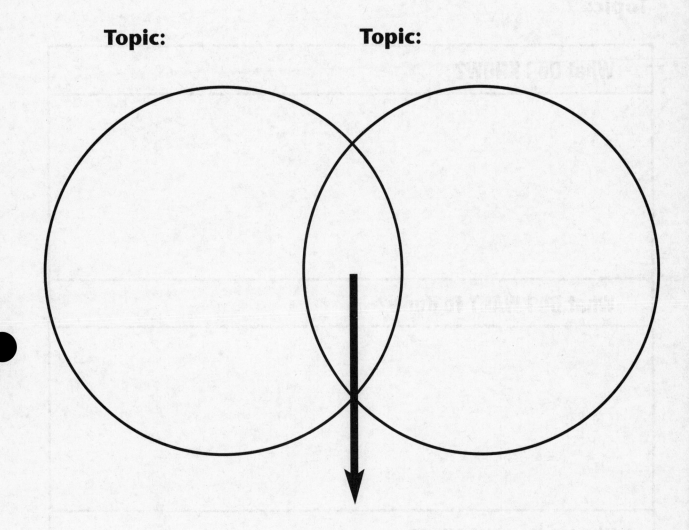

KWL Chart

Topic:

What Do I KNOW?
What Do I WANT to Know?
What Have I LEARNED?

What's the Difference?

In the course of the day, you probably have encountered animals and other types of organisms.

1. Make a list of five animals that you saw today.

2. Then, make a list of five organisms other than animals that you saw today.

3. What characteristics do animals have that the other types of organisms do not?

ANSWERS
1. Examples include humans, dogs, grasshoppers, birds, squirrels.
2. Examples include trees, grass, mushrooms, shrubs, moss.
3. Animals cannot make their own food while plants and fungi can. Animals generally can move from place to place while plants and fungi cannot.

© Pearson Education, Inc.

26–1 Introduction to the Animal Kingdom

A. What Is an Animal?

B. What Animals Do to Survive

1. Feeding

2. Respiration

3. Circulation

4. Excretion

5. Response

6. Movement

7. Reproduction

C. Trends in Animal Evolution

1. Cell Specialization and Levels of Organization

2. Early Development

3. Body Symmetry

4. Cephalization

5. Body Cavity Formation

© Pearson Education, Inc.

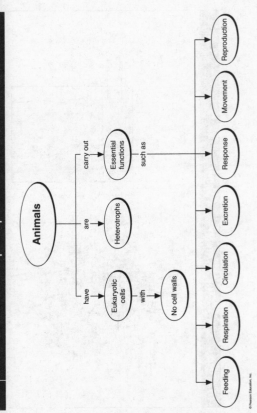

© Pearson Education, Inc.

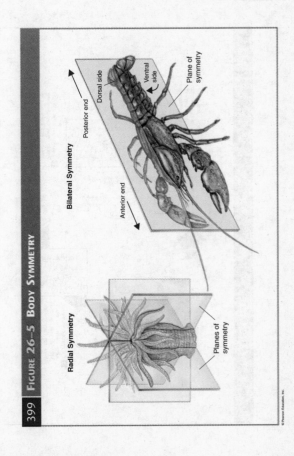

© Pearson Education, Inc.

No Sinking or Swimming

You likely have a green, yellow, blue, or pink sponge in your kitchen sink at home. This is a synthetic (human-made) sponge, not a natural sponge. But you may have used a natural sponge in the bath or when washing the car. These sponges are usually brownish and are irregularly shaped.

1. Natural sponges live in the water, and are attached to a single spot. Although they cannot move from place to place like many other animals, sponges are still animals. Because they are animals, what characteristics must sponges have?

2. What characteristics does a kitchen sponge have? Which of these characteristics do you think a natural sponge has?

26–2 Sponges

A. What Is a Sponge?

B. Form and Function in Sponges

   1. Body Plan

   2. Feeding

   3. Respiration, Circulation, and Excretion

   4. Response

   5. Reproduction

C. Ecology of Sponges

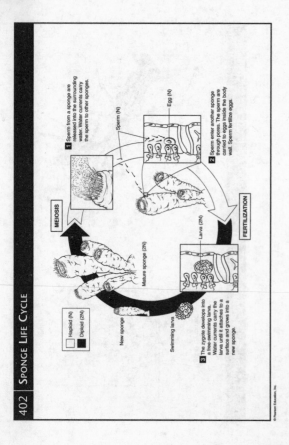

402 | SPONGE LIFE CYCLE

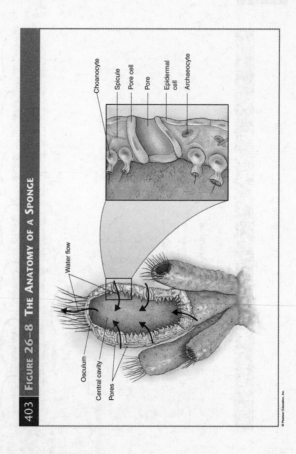

403 | FIGURE 26–8 THE ANATOMY OF A SPONGE

What's in a Name?

Perhaps you have heard about creatures called jellyfishes on television, in school, or at an aquarium; maybe you live near the ocean and have actually seen jellyfishes.

1. Do jellyfishes look like what their name describes? Make a simple drawing of what you think a jellyfish looks like.

2. Some scientists suggest that jellyfishes should be called "jellies." What might this new name tell you about jellyfishes?

ANSWERS
1. Students should draw stacks animals with tentacles.
2. This new name suggests that these animals have jelly-like bodies, but they are not fish.

26–3 Cnidarians

A. What Is a Cnidarian?

B. Form and Function in Cnidarians

   1. Body Plan

   2. Feeding

   3. Respiration, Circulation, and Excretion

   4. Response

   5. Movement

   6. Reproduction

C. Groups of Cnidarians

   1. Jellyfishes

   2. Hydras and Their Relatives

   3. Sea Anemones and Corals

D. Ecology of Corals

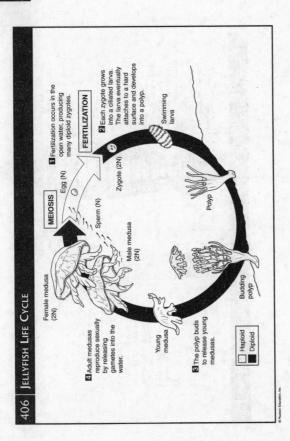

406 | JELLYFISH LIFE CYCLE

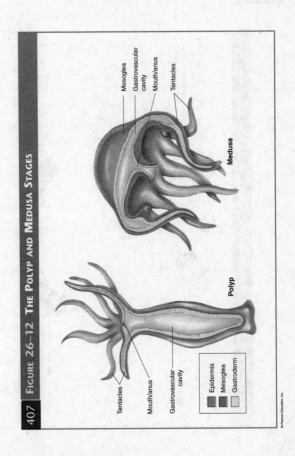

407 | FIGURE 26–12 THE POLYP AND MEDUSA STAGES

Tapeworm Tales

Have you ever heard someone say, "That person eats so much and stays so thin, you'd think he has a tapeworm!"

1. In the United States, the chance of having a tapeworm in your body is very rare. From clues in the above statement, how might a tapeworm affect an individual? Where would you most likely find a tapeworm in the body?

2. On what do you think these tapeworms feed?

ANSWERS
1. The tapeworm might cause the person to lose weight or might result in an intestinal blockage. The tapeworm lives in the intestines of its host.
2. Food digested by its host

© Pearson Education, Inc.

27–1 Flatworms

A. What Is a Flatworm?

B. Form and Function in Flatworms

  1. Feeding

  2. Respiration, Circulation, and Excretion

  3. Response

  4. Movement

  5. Reproduction

C. Groups of Flatworms

  1. Turbellarians

  2. Flukes

  3. Tapeworms

© Pearson Education, Inc.

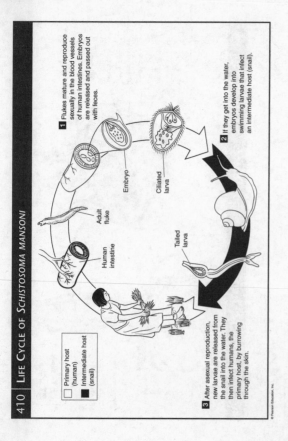

1 Flukes mature and reproduce sexually in the blood vessels of human intestines. Embryos are released and passed out with feces.

2 If they get into the water, embryos develop into swimming larvae that infect an intermediate host (snail).

3 After asexual reproduction, new larvae are released from the snail into the water. They then infect humans, the primary host, by burrowing through the skin.

Adult fluke

Embryo

Ciliated larva

Tailed larva

Human intestine

☐ Primary host (human)

■ Intermediate host (snail)

© Pearson Education, Inc.

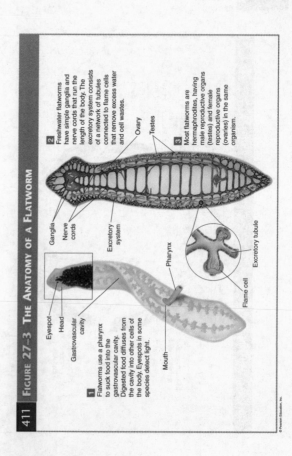

2 Freshwater flatworms have simple ganglia and nerve cords that run the length of the body. The excretory system consists of a network of tubules connected to flame cells that remove excess water and cell wastes.

3 Most flatworms are hermaphrodites, having male reproductive organs (testes) and female reproductive organs (ovaries) in the same organism.

1 Flatworms use a pharynx to suck food into the gastrovascular cavity. Digested food diffuses from the cavity into other cells of the body. Eyespots in some species detect light.

Ovary

Testes

Ganglia

Nerve cords

Excretory system

Pharynx

Eyespot

Head

Gastrovascular cavity

Mouth

Flame cell

Excretory tubule

© Pearson Education, Inc.

Too Small to Measure Up?

When digging in the soil, you can see many animals, such as insects, earthworms, and spiders. But there are many animals that you cannot see. Roundworms, for example, are so small that a shovelful of fertile soil may contain millions of these free-living worms.

1. To see how long roundworms are, draw a line on a sheet of paper. The width of the line that you drew is the length of the shortest roundworms. Measure and record the width of the line.

2. The width of the tip of your pinky finger is the length of the longest roundworms. Measure and record the width of your pinky.

3. Based on this information, what is the range of length in roundworms?

ANSWERS
1. About 0.2 millimeters
2. About 6 millimeters
3. From 0.2 to 6 millimeters

© Pearson Education, Inc.

27–2 Roundworms

A. What Is a Roundworm?

B. Form and Function in Roundworms

   1. Feeding

   2. Respiration, Circulation, and Excretion

   3. Response

   4. Movement

   5. Reproduction

C. Roundworms and Human Disease

   1. Trichinosis-Causing Worms

   2. Filarial Worms

   3. Ascarid Worms

   4. Hookworms

D. Research on *C. elegans*

© Pearson Education, Inc.

ORGANISM	DISEASE	ROUTE OF INFECTION	DESCRIPTION
Trichinella	Trichinosis	Eating undercooked meat containing larval cysts	Larvae burrow into tissues of host, causing pain
Filarial worms	Elephantiasis	Bite of insect carrying filarial worms	Worms block passage of fluids within lymph vessels, causing tissues to swell
Ascaris	*Ascaris* infection/ infestation	Eating unwashed food contaminated with *Ascaris*	Worms in intestine block normal passage of food and absorption of nutrients
Hookworms	Hookworm infection/ infestation	Bare skin in contact with contaminated soil	Worms attach to intestinal wall and suck blood, causing weakness and poor growth

© Pearson Education, Inc.

Just Slinking or Wriggling in the Rain

Have you ever noticed that after a spring rain, earthworms come out of the soil and appear on driveways, in puddles, and on sidewalks? Why does this happen?

1. An earthworm breathes through its skin. If its skin dries out, it cannot breathe. Why would an earthworm be more likely to "surface" during the rain than at other times?

2. What types of weather conditions might be fatal for an earthworm?

ANSWERS
1. The rain keeps the skin of the earthworm moist. At other times, the earthworm is likely to dry out and suffocate.
2. Hot and dry weather is fatal for an earthworm because its skin dries out quickly.

© Pearson Education, Inc.

27–3 Annelids

A. What Is an Annelid?

B. Form and Function in Annelids

   1. Feeding and Digestion

   2. Circulation

   3. Respiration

   4. Excretion

   5. Response

   6. Movement

   7. Reproduction

C. Groups of Annelids

   1. Oligochaetes

   2. Leeches

   3. Polychaetes

D. Ecology of Annelids

© Pearson Education, Inc.

Comparing Flatworms, Roundworms, and Annelids

CHARACTERISTIC	FLATWORMS	ROUNDWORMS	ANNELIDS
Shape	Flattened	Cylindrical with tapering ends	Cylindrical with tapering ends
Segmentation	No	No	Yes
Body cavity	Acoelomate	Pseudocoelomate	Coelomate
Digestion and excretion	Gastrovascular cavity with one opening only; flame cells remove metabolic wastes	Tube-within-a-tube digestive tract; opening at each end; metabolic wastes excreted through body wall	Tube-within-a-tube digestive tract; opening at each end; nephridia remove metabolic wastes
Respiration	Through skin; no respiratory organs	Through skin; no respiratory organs	Through skin; aquatic annelids breathe through gills
Circulation	No heart, blood vessels, or blood	No heart, blood vessels, or blood	Blood circulated through blood vessels in closed circulatory system
Response	Simple brain; nerve cords run length of body; eyespot and other specialized cells that detect stimuli	Several ganglia in head region; nerve cords run length of body; several types of sense organs	Well-developed nervous system with brain and several nerve cords; many sense organs
Movement	Gliding, twisting, and turning	Thrashing	Forward peristaltic movement
Reproduction	Sexual (hermaphrodites); asexual (fission)	Sexual (primary males and females)	Sexual (some are hermaphrodites; some have separate sexes)

© Pearson Education, Inc.

Figure 27–16 The Anatomy of an Earthworm

Labels: Setae, Mouth, Brain, Ganglion, Ventral blood vessel, Dorsal blood vessel, Reproductive organs, Crop, Ring vessels, Gizzard, Ganglia, Body segments, Nephridia, Longitudinal muscle, Circular muscle, Anus, Clitellum

ANSWERS
1. Both the clam and the octopus have soft bodies and legs in water.
2. The clam has a shell, whereas the octopus does not. The octopus has tentacles, whereas the clam does not.

© Pearson Education, Inc.

The Same Yet Different

Have you ever eaten clams? Gone clamming? Seen clams in the supermarket? How about octopi? Have you ever seen an octopus in a movie or in an aquarium?

1. Clams and octopi are members of the phylum Mollusca. Although they have similarities, they have some differences, too. What is one characteristic they share?

2. What is one way that these animals differ from one another?

© Pearson Education, Inc.

27-4 Mollusks

A. What Is a Mollusk?

B. Form and Function in Mollusks

    1. Body Plan

    2. Feeding

    3. Respiration

    4. Circulation

    5. Excretion

    6. Response

    7. Movement

    8. Reproduction

C. Groups of Mollusks

    1. Gastropods

    2. Bivalves

    3. Cephalopods

D. Ecology of Mollusks

Comparing the Three Major Groups of Mollusks

MOLLUSK GROUP	SHELL	FOOT	EXAMPLES
Gastropods	Shell-less or single-shelled	Muscular foot located on ventral side and used for movement	Snail, slug, sea hare, nudibranch
Bivalves	Two shells held together by one or two muscles	Burrowing species have muscular foot. Surface-dwelling species have either no foot or a "reduced" foot.	Clam, oyster, mussel, scallop
Cephalopods	Internal shell or no shell	Head is attached to a single foot. The foot is divided into tentacles or arms.	Octopus, squid, cuttlefish, nautilus

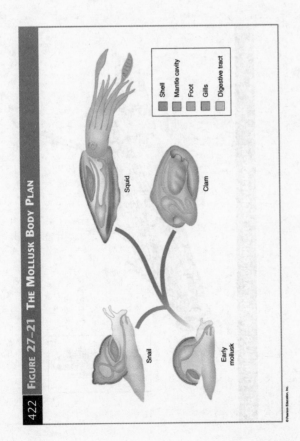

422 FIGURE 27-21 THE MOLLUSK BODY PLAN

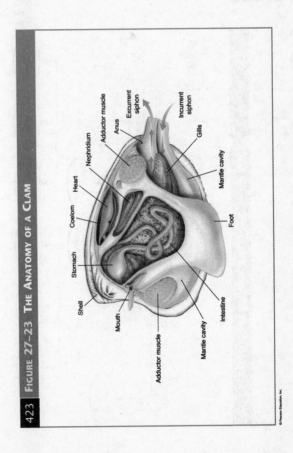

423 FIGURE 27-23 THE ANATOMY OF A CLAM

Hard on the Outside but Soft on the Inside

Some animals, such as humans, are soft on the outside but have endoskeletons. Other animals, such as insects and spiders, have exoskeletons. If you've ever had to wear a cast while a broken bone healed, you have some idea of what an exoskeleton is like. Imagine that you have a cast on your thumb.

1. List two ways that a cast can protect your thumb and your skin cannot.

2. What functions might an exoskeleton have for insects and spiders?

3. How would a cast on your thumb affect the way you use your hand?

4. Do you think an exoskeleton has the same limitations? Explain your answer.

ANSWERS
1. Possible answers: protect it from scrapes, stings, and splinters
2. Protect and support the body, and prevent loss of body water
3. The cast would limit flexibility.
4. Students will likely say that the exoskeleton does limit mobility. Students may know that an exoskeleton is jointed, allowing bending in specific places.

© Pearson Education, Inc.

28–1 Introduction to the Arthropods

   A. What Is an Arthropod?

   B. Evolution of Arthropods

   C. Form and Function in Arthropods

      1. Feeding

      2. Respiration

      3. Circulation

      4. Excretion

      5. Response

      6. Movement

      7. Reproduction

   D. Growth and Development in Arthropods

© Pearson Education, Inc.

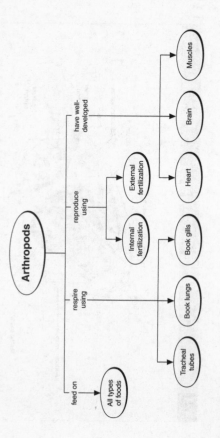

© Pearson Education, Inc.

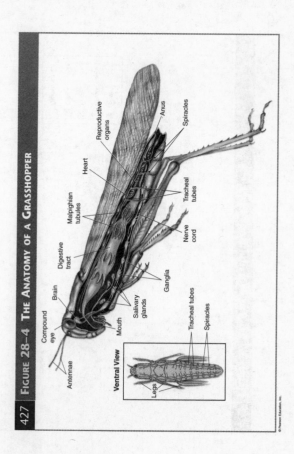

© Pearson Education, Inc.

Form Fits Function to Snag a Speeding Insect

You probably know that spiders spin webs. And you may have seen a spider lowering itself by a single slender thread. But did you know that spiders make as many as seven different types of silk threads?

1. For what functions might spiders spin silk threads?

2. The type of spider silk used in the center of webs is called capture silk. It is very stretchy. Why might stretchy silk fit this function well?

3. The type of silk spiders use to lower themselves is called dragline silk. It is not very stretchy. Why might less-stretchy silk fit this function well?

ANSWERS
1. Possible answers: cocoons for eggs and wrappings for prey.
2. Stretchy silk lets the insects bounce back and forth. The prey hits, "hanging on to it. Prey might bounce off a stiff web.
3. Spiders can lower themselves with more precision if their "dragline" does not stretch too much.

© Pearson Education, Inc.

28–2 Groups of Arthropods

  A. Crustaceans

  B. Spiders and Their Relatives

    1. Horseshoe Crabs

    2. Spiders

    3. Mites and Ticks

    4. Scorpions

  C. Insects and Their Relatives

    1. Centipedes

    2. Millipedes

© Pearson Education, Inc.

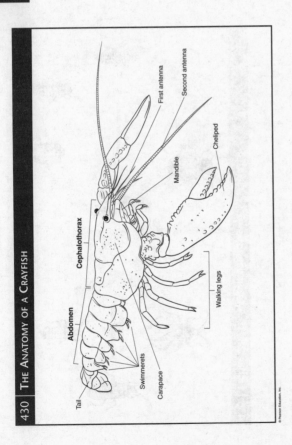

430 | THE ANATOMY OF A CRAYFISH

© Pearson Education, Inc.

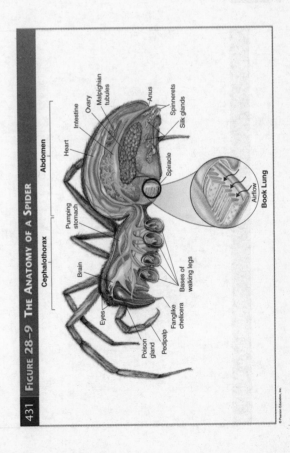

431 | FIGURE 28–9 THE ANATOMY OF A SPIDER

© Pearson Education, Inc.

What's in a Name?

Like all arthropods, insects have segmented bodies, tough exoskeletons, and jointed appendages. What makes them different from other arthropods is that insects have bodies divided into three parts—head, thorax, and abdomen. They also have three pairs of legs attached to their thoraxes.

Working in a group, each group member should perform the following activity.

1. On a sheet of paper, make a sketch of an insect that you have seen around school or at home. Below your drawing, list those features that allow the insect to be successful in its habitat.

2. What features does the insect have that help it survive?

3. How many features did your group's insects have in common? What were these features?

4. Describe the positive and negative impacts that these features have on humans.

5. What is meant by the statement, "Of all the animals, insects have had the greatest impact on the activities of this planet"?

28–3 Insects

   A. What Is an Insect?

      1. Responses to Stimuli

      2. Adaptations for Feeding

      3. Movement and Flight

      4. Metamorphosis

   B. Insects and Humans

   C. Insect Communication

   D. Insect Societies

      1. Castes

      2. Communication in Societies

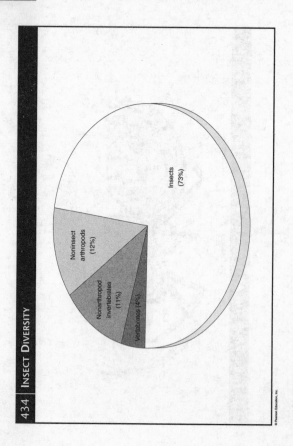

434 INSECT DIVERSITY

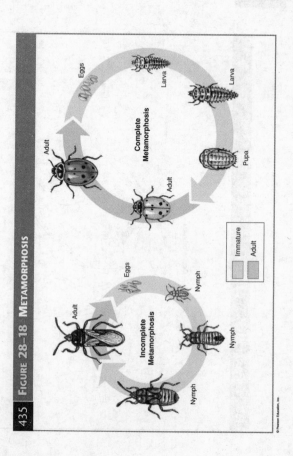

435 FIGURE 28–18 METAMORPHOSIS

If You Were a Two-Sided Animal...

Imagine that you were an animal like no other in the animal kingdom. You have no head and no tail. However, you have two sides, with your toothless mouth on one side. You have no arms or legs, and your body is shaped like a disc.

1. Briefly describe the type of environment in which you would be most likely to survive. Why do you think you would live in this type of environment?

2. What types of food would you likely eat? Explain your answer.

3. What species name would you give yourself?

28–4 Echinoderms

A. What Is an Echinoderm?

B. Form and Function in Echinoderms

1. Feeding

2. Respiration and Circulation

3. Excretion

4. Response

5. Movement

6. Reproduction

C. Groups of Echinoderms

1. Sea Urchins and Sand Dollars

2. Brittle Stars

3. Sea Cucumbers

4. Sea Stars

5. Sea Lilies and Feather Stars

D. Ecology of Echinoderms

Comparing Groups and Major Characteristics of Echinoderms

Characteristic	Sea urchins and sand dollars	Brittle stars	Sea cucumbers	Sea stars	Sea lilies and feather stars
Feeding	Detritivores	Detritivores	Detritivores	Most carnivores	Herbivores
Shape	Disc- or globe-shaped, no arms	Star-shaped, arms	Cucumber-shaped, no arms	Star-shaped, arms	Stalk with feathery arms
Movement	Burrow in sandy ocean bottom or wedge in rock crevices using moveable spines attached to endoskeleton	Move rapidly along ocean floor using arms	Move slowly along ocean floor using muscular body wall to crawl	Creep slowly along ocean floor using arms	Cannot move; attached to ocean bottom

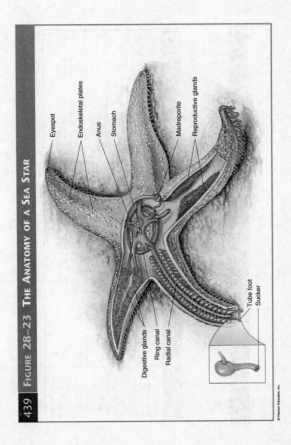

Eyespot
Endoskeletal plates
Anus
Stomach
Madreporite
Reproductive glands
Digestive glands
Ring canal
Radial canal
Tube foot
Sucker

Seeing Symmetry

A dictionary would define symmetry as a "similar distribution of parts." But what does this mean?

1. On a sheet of paper, draw the outline of a natural sponge, a sea star, and an earthworm. Try to draw a line dividing each in half so that the two halves are mirror images of each other. With which organisms can you do this? With which can you not?

2. Which of the above organisms are symmetrical? Which is asymmetrical?

3. Try to divide each of the symmetrical organisms in half again but in a different way so that each half is the mirror image of the other. With which organism can you do this? This organism is radially symmetrical. With which can you not? This organism is bilaterally symmetrical.

ANSWERS
1. Students should be able to divide the sea star and earthworm in half, but not the sponge.
2. The sea star and earthworm are symmetrical. The natural sponge is asymmetrical.
3. Sea star (radially symmetrical); earthworm (bilaterally symmetrical)

29–1 Invertebrate Evolution

A. Origin of the Invertebrates

   1. The First Multicellular Animals

   2. Beginnings of Invertebrate Diversity

B. Invertebrate Phylogeny

C. Evolutionary Trends

   1. Specialized Cells, Tissues, and Organs

   2. Body Symmetry

   3. Cephalization

   4. Segmentation

   5. Coelom Formation

   6. Embryological Development

Comparing Invertebrates

Major Characteristics	Sponges	Cnidarians	Flatworms	Roundworms	Annelids	Mollusks	Arthropods	Echinoderms
Germ Layers	Absent	Two	Three	Three	Three	Three	Three	Three
Body Symmetry	Absent	Radial	Bilateral	Bilateral	Bilateral	Bilateral	Bilateral	Radial (adults)
Cephalization	Absent	Absent	Present	Present	Present	Present	Present	Absent (adults)
Coelom	Absent	Absent	Absent	Pseudocoelom	True coelom	True coelom	True coelom	True coelom
Early Development	—	—	Protostome	Protostome	Protostome	Protostome	Protostome	Deuterostome

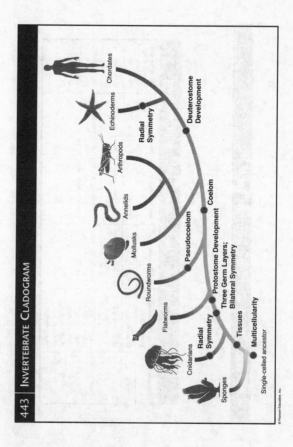

Change, Change, and More Change

Develop a list of eight invertebrate phyla. Next to each phylum, list a representative animal, the animal's habitat, and any special adaptations found in the animal. Then, discuss the following with your partner.

1. What adaptations are found in aquatic invertebrates that are not found in terrestrial invertebrates?

2. As animals moved from an aquatic environment to a terrestrial environment, which systems do you think would have undergone the most change? Explain your answer.

3. How do you think the development of an anterior, or head, end affected animals?

29–2 Form and Function in Invertebrates

A. Feeding and Digestion
   1. Intracellular and Extracellular Digestion
   2. Patterns of Extracellular Digestion
B. Respiration
   1. Aquatic Invertebrates
   2. Terrestrial Invertebrates
C. Circulation
   1. Open Circulatory Systems
   2. Closed Circulatory Systems
D. Excretion
   1. Aquatic Invertebrates
   2. Terrestrial Invertebrates
E. Response
   1. Centralization and Cephalization
   2. Specialization
F. Movement and Support
   1. Hydrostatic Skeletons
   2. Exoskeletons
   3. Endoskeletons
G. Sexual and Asexual Reproduction

---

446 | **Section 29–2** Types of Invertebrate Skeletons

Type of Skeleton	Sponges	Cnidarians	Flatworms	Roundworms	Annelids	Mollusks	Arthropods	Echinoderms
Hydrostatic		X	X	X	X	Some		
Exoskeleton						Some (shells)	X	
Endoskeleton	Simple (spicules or spongin)							X

---

447 | **FIGURE 29–8 INVERTEBRATE DIGESTIVE SYSTEMS**

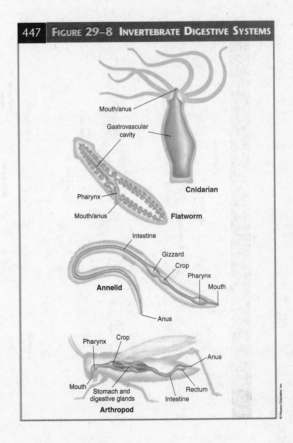

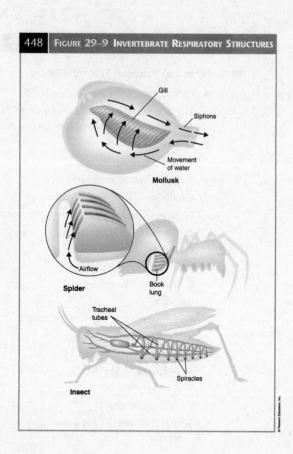

Gill

Siphons

Movement of water

Mollusk

Airflow

Spider

Book lung

Tracheal tubes

Spiracles

Insect

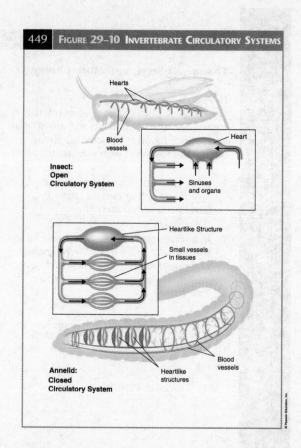

Hearts

Blood vessels

Insect: Open Circulatory System

Heart

Sinuses and organs

Heartlike Structure

Small vessels in tissues

Annelid: Closed Circulatory System

Heartlike structures

Blood vessels

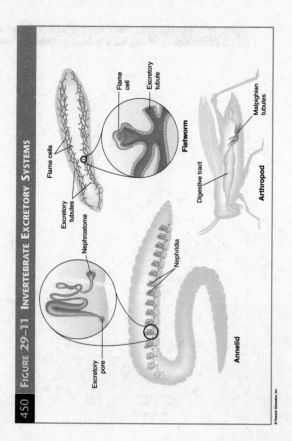

Flame cell

Excretory tubule

Flame cells

Excretory tubules

Nephrostome

Flatworm

Malpighian tubules

Digestive tract

Arthropod

Nephridia

Excretory pore

Annelid

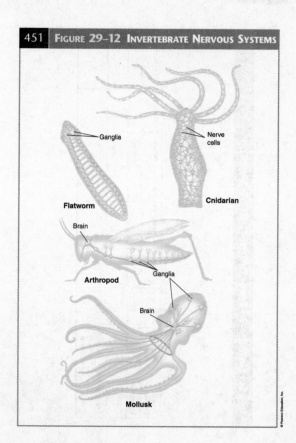

Ganglia

Nerve cells

Flatworm

Cnidarian

Brain

Arthropod

Ganglia

Brain

Mollusk